Pat Thomas

BASIC SKILLS IN MATHEMATICS/Book 3

BASIC SKILLS IN MATHEMATICS/Book 3

R W Fox

Deputy Headmaster, Fort Luton Secondary School for Boys, Chatham, Kent

Edward Arnold

First published 1975
by Edward Arnold (Publishers) Ltd
41 Bedford Square
London WC1B 3DQ
Reprinted 1976, 1977, Twice 1978, 1979

ISBN: 0 7131 0002 8

Also available:

Answers to BASIC SKILLS IN
MATHEMATICS/Book 3

By the same author:

Certificate Mathematics
A complete course in 3 books to CSE and O Level;

Mathematical Tables and Data
In collaboration with H. A. Shaw.

Printed in Great Britain by
Unwin Brothers Ltd, Woking & London

Contents

1 **Simple revision tests** 1

2 **Revision exercises – arithmetic** 4
Four rules of number
Four rules of decimals
The metric system
Factors – HCF and LCM
Fractions – lowest terms, mixed numbers, improper fractions
Four rules of fractions and mixed numbers
Rectangles – perimeter and area
Volumes of cuboids
The calendar

3 **Revision exercises – algebra** 11
Collecting like terms
Substitution
Equations
Powers – index numbers

4 **Buying from a catalogue** 13
Four rules of money

5 **Averages** 16

6 **Geometry** 17
The quadrilateral
The parallelogram
The rhombus
The rectangle
The square
Things to remember

7 **Area** 23
Areas of rectangles by subtraction
Area of a parallelogram
Area of a triangle

8 **Algebra** 34
More about simple equations
Directed numbers
Directed numbers – addition and subtraction
Rule of signs

9 **More about decimal and vulgar fractions** 44
Approximations
Correct to a given decimal place
Changing decimals to vulgar fractions
Changing vulgar fractions to decimals

10 **Percentage** 50
Fractions or decimals to percentages
Percentages to fractions or decimals
Quantities as percentages

11 **Angles** 54
Revision
Interior and exterior angles of regular and irregular polygons
More facts about angles – parallel lines cut by a transversal

12 **Proportion** 64
Direct proportion
Inverse proportion

13 **Ratio** 67
Increase and decrease in a given ratio
Sharing in a given ratio

14 **Percentage changes** 72
Increase
Decrease

15 **Graphs** 75
Straight-line graphs
Bar-charts
Pie-charts

16 **More work with directed numbers** 80
Revision
Multiplication
Division

7 **Algebra – use of brackets** 84
Addition
Subtraction
Rule of signs
Multiplication
Equations
Using two pairs of brackets
Substitution

8 **Volume** 92
Cubes and cuboids – revision
Solids of uniform cross-section
Volume of solids of uniform cross-section

9 **Construction of solids** 98
Nets for a set of polyhedra
Basic shapes for tracing

20 **Using a ready-reckoner** 105

21 **Algebra – problems** 108
Some brain-teasers to finish the book

Catalogue 111

Preface

It is the author's opinion that modern approaches to the teaching of mathematics frequently do not pursue a particular skill to the point at which a child reaches the *confidence of knowing* that he has mastered the process. Work assignments are often too brief, sacrificing the acquisition of skill for novelty in the names of 'progress' and 'release from boredom'.

Children do not master essential skills incidentally, as some teachers venture to hope. Lack of ability is often due to lack of *sufficient* experience – perhaps the only motivation really needed is the *opportunity* to learn the skills and, for many, this means repeating the processes often enough.

The extensive exercises in this text permit the pupil to dwell on those operations and skills which require more experience before moving on – so avoiding the usual search by the teacher for more material of a similar nature from a variety of textbooks. Some opinions suggest, not without good cause, that mechanical skills have become neglected – this series of books seeks to provide a remedy. There is no shortage of 'activity' material on the market, so the author makes no apologies for the absence of such an approach from this present work. Nevertheless, there is much to keep the pupil's *mind* active.

Book 3 seeks to provide continuous revision of counting, using number, calculating in money and also in length and weight.

The material has been prepared to satisfy the needs of a pupil's mathematical ability rather than his chronological age group. There is ample opportunity for the teacher to practise the professional skills and indeed, such teaching will still be essential with slower pupils. Assistance will almost certainly have to be given to those of poor reading ability.

For those teachers wishing to pursue a 'modern approach' or one of the various 'maths projects', *Basic Skills in Mathematics* will provide a valuable backup course in fundamental processes.

R W F

1 Simple revision tests

	Test 1	*Test 2*	*Test 3*	*Test 4*
1.	5 × 3	18 ÷ 3	9 + 7	3x × 3
2.	8 + 7	11 − 8	8 × 3	8y + 9y
3.	9 − 5	9 × 2	36 ÷ 4	£1.20 × 5
4.	16 ÷ 8	7 + 6	13 − 4	£1.20 ÷ 3
5.	2x + 4x	½ + ½	1·3 × 2	½ × ¼
6.	10y − 3y	1·2 + 1·4	4·8 ÷ 4	1½ + 1½
7.	10a ÷ 2	1 − ¼	3·6 − 1·4	15 − 7
8.	6a × 3	x × x	8x × 4	12 × 0
9.	5cm × 6	4y ÷ y	½ + 1½	½ × ½
10.	20mm ÷ 5	3mg × 7	24g ÷ 2	1 ÷ 2

	Test 5	*Test 6*	*Test 7*	*Test 8*
1.	30p × 9	22mg ÷ 11	5 × 11	14mm + 19mm
2.	17 + 14	¼ × 2	1·2 + 1·9	4y × 4
3.	4x × 5	16 + 18	0·4 × 10	$\frac{5}{8} - \frac{3}{8}$
4.	17g − 8g	2 ÷ 3	¾ − ½	7 × 0
5.	½ + ¼	4x × 2	$\frac{1}{8}$ × 8	1 ÷ 4
6.	4 ÷ 5	2·4 + 1·7	£17 + £18	3·5 + 1·6
7.	35 ÷ 7	0 × 9	33cm ÷ 3	0·7 × 2
8.	y × y	½ ÷ ½	¾ + ¾	$\frac{3}{5} + \frac{2}{5}$
9.	12 × 3	11a × 4	3 ÷ 4	6x ÷ 2
10.	4·6 + 2·4	½ − ¼	3x × 4	50p × 3

	Test 9	*Test 10*	*Test 11*	*Test 12*
1.	£5.50 ÷ 5	18x ÷ 6	½ ÷ 2	1·2 × 6
2.	33cm − 16cm	1·2mg × 9	5 × 0·2	£1.40 + £1.90
3.	¼ + ¼	24 + 17	35mg − 19mg	2½ × 0
4.	0·3 × 100	6·3 − 3·9	4·7 + 2·3	2x × 3
5.	24 × 5	£4.80 ÷ 8	1½ − ¼	¾ + ½
6.	1·3 + 2·8	¾ − ¼	£4.50 ÷ 9	28dl ÷ 7
7.	1½ × 3	6a × 4	2¼ × 4	1¾ − ½
8.	4y × 2	10 × 0	36 + 8	½ × 2
9.	5·4 − 2·8	2·2 + 2·9	90p × 6	0·2 × 1000
10.	16p + 15p	1¼ + 1¼	5·2 − 1·9	5x × 5x

Test 13

1. $2x \times x$
2. $23 + 28$
3. $0{\cdot}6 \times 4$
4. $2\frac{1}{4} - \frac{3}{4}$
5. £2.40 ÷ 3
6. $1\frac{1}{2} \times 4$
7. $123 - 49$
8. $4a \div 4$
9. $\frac{1}{2} \times \frac{1}{4}$
10. $3\frac{1}{4} \times 0$

Test 14

1. £1.60 ÷ 8
2. $3\frac{1}{2} - 1\frac{3}{4}$
3. $2a^2 + 3a^2$
4. $103 - 37$
5. $10 \div 4$
6. $0{\cdot}5 \times 6$
7. $1\frac{2}{3} + 1\frac{2}{3}$
8. $35 + 26$
9. $2\frac{1}{4} \times 8$
10. $2x = 16$

Test 15

1. $1\frac{3}{4} \times 4$
2. $5a \div a$
3. $16 \div 5$
4. $34 + 39$
5. £1.64 + £1.46
6. $3x \times x$
7. $2\frac{3}{4} + 2\frac{3}{4}$
8. $101 - 53$
9. $3\frac{1}{4} - 2\frac{1}{2}$
10. $0{\cdot}06 \times 100$

Test 16

1. $1{\cdot}1 \times 6$
2. $2\frac{2}{3} - 1\frac{1}{3}$
3. $3x = 21$
4. $1\frac{3}{8} + 1\frac{3}{8}$
5. $56 \div 7$
6. $14 \div 3$
7. $0{\cdot}5 \times 10$
8. $1\frac{1}{4} \times 6$
9. $5a^2 - 2a^2$
10. $26 + 48$

Test 17

1. $x^2 \div x$
2. 8×0
3. $1\frac{1}{3} \times 3$
4. $15 \div 2$
5. £1.40 ÷ 2
6. $800 \div 10$
7. $1\frac{2}{3} + 1\frac{1}{6}$
8. $2x \times 2x$
9. $3\frac{1}{3} - 1\frac{2}{3}$
10. $1{\cdot}1 \times 8$

Test 18

1. $37 + 49$
2. $18 \div 4$
3. $4a^2 + 3a^2$
4. $4\frac{3}{5} - 2\frac{1}{5}$
5. $111 - 38$
6. $7g \times 7$
7. $1\frac{1}{6} \times 6$
8. $1\frac{3}{5} + 1\frac{3}{5}$
9. $42p \div 6$
10. $4x = 40$

Test 19

1. £1.20 ÷ 6
2. $3x \times 3x$
3. $20 \div 6$
4. $1\frac{1}{5} \times 5$
5. $96p \div 12$
6. $\frac{2}{3} \times \frac{2}{3}$
7. $27 + 37$
8. $4\frac{1}{5} - 2\frac{3}{5}$
9. $x^3 \div x^2$
10. 6×8

Test 20

1. $8x = 40$
2. $3\frac{5}{6} - 1\frac{1}{2}$
3. £6.30 ÷ 7
4. 8×8
5. $\frac{1}{5} \times \frac{1}{5}$
6. $6a^2 - 4a^2$
7. $1\frac{1}{8} \times 8$
8. $21 \div 9$
9. $32 \div 4$
10. $49 + 38$

Test 21

1. $132 - 64$
2. $1\frac{2}{3} \times 3$
3. $x^2 \div x^2$
4. $\frac{3}{4} \times \frac{3}{4}$
5. $4\frac{1}{2} - 2\frac{1}{6}$
6. $72 \div 9$
7. $1\frac{1}{8} \times 8$
8. £7.70 ÷ 7
9. $25 \div 4$
10. $x^2 \times x$

Test 22

1. $3a^2 + a^2$
2. $40p \div 8$
3. £18 ÷ 5
4. $103 - 59$
5. £8.40 ÷ 12
6. $20 \div 8$
7. $6x = 36$
8. $\frac{3}{4} \times \frac{2}{3}$
9. $57 + 39$
10. $1\frac{2}{5} \times 5$

Test 23

1. $70p \times 4$
2. $112 - 57$
3. $2\frac{1}{3} \times 6$
4. $x^3 \times x^2$
5. $26 \div 4$
6. $53 + 49$
7. $\frac{2}{3} \times \frac{3}{8}$
8. $3x^2 \div x$
9. $5\frac{5}{6} - 3\frac{2}{3}$
10. £3.50 ÷ 7

Test 24

1. $7x = 42$
2. $20 \div 3$
3. £2.10 ÷ 3
4. $66 + 44$
5. $2\frac{1}{8} \times 4$
6. $0{\cdot}7 \times 100$
7. $4\frac{3}{8} - 2\frac{1}{4}$
8. $\frac{3}{5} \times \frac{5}{9}$
9. $5a^2 - a^2$
10. $105 - 69$

	Test 25	*Test 26*	*Test 27*	*Test 28*
1.	£1.80 ÷ 2	6x = 9	0·7 × 10	9¾ ÷ 3
2.	$3\frac{1}{3} \times 6$	0·66 ÷ 1·1	8½ ÷ 2	£1.20 × 11
3.	76 + 34	$3a^2 + 4a^2$	£1.10 × 10	2·2m ÷ 11
4.	8 × 9	11 × 0	$6x^3 - 5x^3$	73 − 37
5.	$4x^3 \div 2x$	0·9 × 10	$2\frac{2}{3} \times \frac{3}{8}$	8x = 44
6.	13x = 39	82 + 28	£2 ÷ 10	87 + 78
7.	$1\frac{1}{2} \times \frac{2}{3}$	1½ × 8	$60^\circ \times 3$	$1\frac{1}{5} \times \frac{5}{6}$
8.	£1.20 × 5	£1.10 ÷ 11	7x = 140	90cg ÷ 10
9.	$120^\circ \div 3$	30mg ÷ 10	12 ÷ 10	$2a^2 \times 3a^3$
10.	12 × 100	$1\frac{1}{3} \times \frac{3}{4}$	64 − 46	£6.30 ÷ 9

	Test 29	*Test 30*	*Test 31*	*Test 32*
1.	10p × 10	£7.70 ÷ 1·1	$2\frac{1}{7} \times 7$	9·9 ÷ 1·1
2.	9x = 30	$6 \times \frac{2}{3}$	£3.60 ÷ 12	76 + 67
3.	42 − 24	11 × 11	321 − 123	£1.10 × 12
4.	3·3g ÷ 3	46 + 64	$3x^2 + 4x^2$	$2\frac{3}{5} - 2\frac{3}{10}$
5.	$4\frac{4}{5} \div 4$	3·7 × 0	9·6 ÷ 1·2	30p × 9
6.	$3\frac{1}{4} + 3\frac{1}{8}$	90m × 9	$2\frac{3}{5} + 2\frac{3}{10}$	$1\frac{3}{5} \times \frac{5}{8}$
7.	80p × 11	$3\frac{1}{3} \times \frac{3}{5}$	8x = 120	543 − 345
8.	$3\frac{1}{4} - 3\frac{1}{8}$	0·2ml × 12	$360^\circ \div 4$	$45^\circ \times 4$
9.	$2\frac{1}{4} \times \frac{4}{9}$	64 − 46	91 + 19	£3.60 ÷ 4
10.	0·06 × 10	12x = 240	7mm × 12	$3\frac{1}{8} \times 8$

	Test 33	*Test 34*	*Test 35*	*Test 36*
1.	7x = 98	$180^\circ \div 4$	1·2 × 9	25x = 100
2.	$5\frac{1}{3} \times 3$	£1.20 × 4	138 − 59	0·5 ÷ 10
3.	0·04 × 10	$3\frac{1}{5} \div \frac{4}{5}$	$3x^2 \times 10x$	$4\frac{1}{3} \times 0$
4.	$12x^3 \div 3x^2$	5x = 75	90p × 6	$2\frac{2}{3} + 1\frac{1}{6}$
5.	85 + 65	0·6 ÷ 30	$2\frac{2}{3} + 1\frac{1}{2}$	£8 ÷ 10
6.	$3\frac{3}{4} - 2\frac{3}{8}$	4·5cg ÷ 9	0·2 × 20	$120^\circ \times 3$
7.	£42 × 0	$3x \times 4x^2$	6x = 96	98 + 67
8.	£4.40 ÷ 11	4¼ × 4	83 + 38	50p × 11
9.	$1\frac{3}{4} + 1\frac{3}{8}$	12 × 8	$1\frac{1}{5} \div \frac{3}{4}$	$2\frac{7}{10} \times 10$
10.	£1.10 × 9	20x = 120	£7.20 ÷ 12	1·2 × 1·2

2 Revision exercises - arithmetic

Four rules of number

Exercise 1

The following are **additions**:

1.	22 34 46	2.	19 30 83	3.	28 47 56	4.	18 47 26
5.	34 46 57	6.	35 24 68	7.	214 325 454	8.	323 232 119
9.	124 235 312	10.	237 218 431	11.	129 436 328	12.	531 137 248

Exercise 2

The following are **subtractions**:

1.	43 26	2.	52 15	3.	65 28	4.	88 49
5.	131 116	6.	283 167	7.	385 196	8.	434 225
9.	684 495	10.	851 484	11.	376 297	12.	565 488

Exercise 3

The following are **long multiplications**:

1. 41 × 23	2. 28 × 25	3. 24 × 16	4. 56 × 27
5. 28 × 21	6. 65 × 34	7. 173 × 41	8. 192 × 53
9. 314 × 18	10. 345 × 35	11. 524 × 21	12. 718 × 42

Exercise 4

The following are **long divisions**:

1. 230 ÷ 46	2. 324 ÷ 54	3. 456 ÷ 76	4. 368 ÷ 92
5. 437 ÷ 23	6. 486 ÷ 27	7. 984 ÷ 41	8. 765 ÷ 45
9. 2394 ÷ 63	10. 4823 ÷ 91	11. 2178 ÷ 121	12. 4424 ÷ 316

Four rules of decimals

Exercise 5

The following are **additions**:

1. 48·23 5·063 15·46 0·772	2. 59·35 8·002 10·26 4·724	3. 9·023 35·54 8·078 74·002	4. 28·35 7·483 36·74 18·06
5. 29·04 17·823 10·006 63·207	6. 82·26 50·007 0·283 32·06	7. 39·53 40·078 2·343 69·008	8. 22·005 30·29 0·863 45·206
9. 61·07 28·563 0·908 35·77	10. 54·96 37·505 8·006 54·79	11. 81·05 23·009 0·807 33·65	12. 35·61 54·006 21·08 10·06

Exercise 6

The following are **subtractions**:

1. 34·874 27·206	2. 48·423 36·645	3. 52·246 48·324	4. 63·724 52·846
5. 102·68 83·06	6. 326·07 209·84	7. 407·94 308·08	8. 304·08 280·05

9.	416·7	**10.**	562·04	**11.**	61·001	**12.**	75·07
	307·56		418·812		47·0183		58·008

Exercise 7

The following are **multiplications by 10, 100, 1000**:

1.	8·7 × 10	**2.**	5·03 × 10	**3.**	8·76 × 100	**4.**	5·6 × 100
5.	9·001 × 1000	**6.**	0·12 × 100	**7.**	6·21 × 1000	**8.**	7·8 × 1000
9.	0·301 × 100	**10.**	0·08 × 1000	**11.**	0·05 × 10	**12.**	0·08 × 100

The following are **long multiplications**:

13.	3·8 × 1·2	**14.**	4·3 × 1·5	**15.**	2·7 × 1·6	**16.**	5·6 × 1·3
17.	12·4 × 1·4	**18.**	17·3 × 1·7	**19.**	27·5 × 2·4	**20.**	92 × 0·81
21.	51·5 × 2·35	**22.**	4·18 × 2·46	**23.**	0·83 × 0·66	**24.**	5·07 × 0·06

Exercise 8

The following are **divisions by 10, 100, 1000**:

1.	35 ÷ 10	**2.**	33·6 ÷ 10	**3.**	536 ÷ 10	**4.**	478 ÷ 100
5.	693 ÷ 1000	**6.**	5317 ÷ 100	**7.**	9345 ÷ 1000	**8.**	536·7 ÷ 1000
9.	87·4 ÷ 100	**10.**	39·6 ÷ 10	**11.**	4·21 ÷ 1000	**12.**	54·6 ÷ 1000

The following are **long divisions**:

13.	4·8 ÷ 3·2	**14.**	5·32 ÷ 3·8	**15.**	5·06 ÷ 2·2	**16.**	14·64 ÷ 1·2
17.	6 ÷ 2·4	**18.**	20·44 ÷ 1·4	**19.**	17·92 ÷ 0·8	**20.**	0·308 ÷ 0·11
21.	0·476 ÷ 3·4	**22.**	2·296 ÷ 16·4	**23.**	7·268 ÷ 3·16	**24.**	23·848 ÷ 5·42

The metric system

kilo hecto deca metre deci centi milli

Exercise 9

Turn the following into **millimetres (mm)**:

1.	2cm	**2.**	0·7cm	**3.**	1·3cm	**4.**	0·64cm
5.	3·6dm	**6.**	5dm	**7.**	33·5cm	**8.**	0·75dm
9.	3m	**10.**	4km	**11.**	4·21m	**12.**	0·042km

Turn the following into **centimetres (cm)**:

13.	100mm	**14.**	3dm	**15.**	46mm	**16.**	4mm
17.	367mm	**18.**	8·2dm	**19.**	0·75dm	**20.**	4m

21.	0·8dm	**22.**	0·6m	**23.**	0·06dm	**24.**	3·2km

Turn the following into **decimetres (dm)**:

25.	98 cm	**26.**	900mm	**27.**	10·6cm	**28.**	734mm
29.	3·43cm	**30.**	0·925cm	**31.**	4·2m	**32.**	1000mm
33.	0·05km	**34.**	71·8cm	**35.**	0·08m	**36.**	2·3km

Exercise 10

Turn the following into **kilograms (kg)**:

1.	1000g	**2.**	100mg	**3.**	10dg	**4.**	10000cg
5.	100dag	**6.**	5·8hg	**7.**	12·5dg	**8.**	500g
9.	8hg 6g	**10.**	7dag 6dg	**11.**	5 000 000 mg	**12.**	9g 15mg

Turn the following into **grams (g)**:

13.	100dg	**14.**	1000cg	**15.**	10 000mg	**16.**	0·05kg
17.	0·5dag	**18.**	0·03hg	**19.**	25·4cg	**20.**	43·2dg
21.	1·2kg	**22.**	5·6dag	**23.**	125cg	**24.**	678·4dg

Turn the following into **litres (l)**:

25.	1kl	**26.**	1ml	**27.**	10cl	**28.**	10hl
29.	100dl	**30.**	100dal	**31.**	0·001kl	**32.**	0·001hl
33.	22·5cl	**34.**	5·34dl	**35.**	725ml	**36.**	4·87dal

Factors – HCF and LCM

Exercise 11

Express the following in **prime factors** using **index numbers** (powers) where possible:

1.	6	**2.**	8	**3.**	9	**4.**	12	**5.**	15
6.	16	**7.**	18	**8.**	20	**9.**	24	**10.**	36
11.	48	**12.**	60	**13.**	72	**14.**	84	**15.**	100
16.	144	**17.**	360	**18.**	2700				

Exercise 12

In each of the following groups of numbers find the **HCF**:

1.	2, 4, 6	**2.**	4, 6, 10	**3.**	6, 9, 12	**4.**	6, 12, 18
5.	12, 18, 24	**6.**	9, 12, 24	**7.**	10, 20, 30	**8.**	20, 30, 45
9.	18, 27, 36	**10.**	14, 21, 49	**11.**	28, 35, 42	**12.**	50, 100, 125

Exercise 13

In each of the following groups of numbers find the **LCM**:

1. 2, 3, 4 **2.** 2, 4, 6 **3.** 2, 3, 6 **4.** 3, 4, 6
5. 2, 4, 8 **6.** 2, 3, 8 **7.** 3, 4, 8 **8.** 6, 8, 12
9. 3, 4, 9 **10.** 3, 5, 9 **11.** 3, 6, 8 **12.** 5, 10, 15
13. 5, 9, 15 **14.** 5, 8, 16 **15.** 4, 5, 9 **16.** 12, 24, 36

Fractions – lowest terms, mixed numbers, improper fractions

Exercise 14

Reduce the following fractions to **lowest terms** (cancel):

1. $\frac{4}{8}$ **2.** $\frac{6}{8}$ **3.** $\frac{4}{12}$ **4.** $\frac{6}{12}$ **5.** $\frac{10}{15}$

6. $\frac{15}{20}$ **7.** $\frac{12}{16}$ **8.** $\frac{18}{24}$ **9.** $\frac{18}{30}$ **10.** $\frac{24}{30}$

11. $\frac{30}{48}$ **12.** $\frac{48}{60}$ **13.** $\frac{54}{60}$ **14.** $\frac{60}{72}$ **15.** $\frac{45}{60}$

Exercise 15

Express the following **improper fractions** as **mixed numbers**:

1. $\frac{7}{2}$ **2.** $\frac{8}{3}$ **3.** $\frac{9}{4}$ **4.** $\frac{11}{5}$ **5.** $\frac{12}{7}$

6. $\frac{15}{8}$ **7.** $\frac{16}{9}$ **8.** $\frac{18}{5}$ **9.** $\frac{20}{3}$ **10.** $\frac{23}{4}$

11. $\frac{21}{12}$ **12.** $\frac{33}{15}$ **13.** $\frac{40}{24}$ **14.** $\frac{60}{48}$ **15.** $\frac{96}{60}$

Exercise 16

Express the following **mixed numbers** as **improper fractions**:

1. $1\frac{3}{4}$ **2.** $3\frac{1}{3}$ **3.** $4\frac{3}{4}$ **4.** $2\frac{4}{5}$ **5.** $2\frac{1}{2}$

6. $8\frac{1}{4}$ **7.** $6\frac{2}{5}$ **8.** $5\frac{2}{3}$ **9.** $3\frac{1}{7}$ **10.** $1\frac{9}{10}$

11. $12\frac{3}{4}$ **12.** $10\frac{3}{5}$ **13.** $9\frac{5}{6}$ **14.** $7\frac{3}{8}$ **15.** $3\frac{5}{16}$

Four rules of fractions and mixed numbers

Exercise 17

The following are **additions** and **subtractions**: (*take care with the signs and use whole numbers first*).

1. $1\frac{1}{2} + 1\frac{3}{4} + 1\frac{1}{8}$
2. $1\frac{2}{3} + 1\frac{1}{2} + 1\frac{5}{6}$
3. $1\frac{3}{5} + 1\frac{1}{2} + 1\frac{7}{10}$
4. $2\frac{1}{3} + 2\frac{1}{2} - 2\frac{3}{4}$
5. $2\frac{1}{6} + 2\frac{1}{4} - 2\frac{2}{3}$
6. $2\frac{1}{2} + 2\frac{1}{4} - 2\frac{5}{6}$
7. $3\frac{5}{8} - 2\frac{3}{4} + 1\frac{1}{2}$
8. $2\frac{3}{4} - 3\frac{1}{2} + 1\frac{7}{8}$
9. $1\frac{5}{8} - 2\frac{1}{4} + 3\frac{1}{2}$
10. $4\frac{7}{8} - 1\frac{5}{6} - 1\frac{3}{4}$
11. $4\frac{7}{12} - 2\frac{1}{3} - 1\frac{3}{8}$
12. $4\frac{9}{10} - 1\frac{3}{5} - 2\frac{2}{3}$
13. $1\frac{2}{3} + \frac{5}{6} - 1\frac{4}{5}$
14. $\frac{11}{12} - 1\frac{5}{8} + 1\frac{5}{6}$
15. $1\frac{8}{9} - \frac{3}{4} - \frac{1}{6}$

Exercise 18

The following are **multiplications** and **divisions**: (*take care with the signs and use improper fractions*).

1. $2\frac{1}{2} \times 2\frac{2}{3} \times 1\frac{1}{5}$
2. $1\frac{3}{4} \times 1\frac{1}{5} \times 1\frac{1}{14}$
3. $1\frac{7}{8} \times 1\frac{1}{3} \times 1\frac{3}{5}$
4. $2\frac{2}{3} \div 2\frac{2}{5}$
5. $1\frac{7}{9} \div 1\frac{1}{3}$
6. $3\frac{3}{4} \div 2\frac{1}{2}$
7. $3\frac{1}{5} \times 1\frac{3}{4} \div \frac{7}{15}$
8. $2\frac{1}{4} \times 2\frac{2}{5} \div 3\frac{3}{5}$
9. $3\frac{1}{8} \times 1\frac{3}{5} \div 1\frac{2}{3}$
10. $1\frac{5}{12} \times 1\frac{4}{5} \div 2\frac{4}{15}$
11. $\frac{7}{9} \times 2\frac{5}{11} \times 3\frac{1}{7}$
12. $1\frac{8}{13} \times 5\frac{1}{5} \div \frac{3}{5}$
13. $1\frac{1}{7} \times \frac{15}{16} \times 2\frac{1}{3}$
14. $2\frac{1}{5} \times 1\frac{11}{14} \div 3\frac{1}{7}$
15. $2\frac{1}{3} \times 1\frac{1}{21} \times \frac{9}{11}$

Rectangles -- perimeter and area

Exercise 19

Given the **length** and the **breadth**, find the **perimeters** and the **areas** of the following rectangles:

1. 3m by 2m
2. 5cm by 4cm
3. 7km by 6km

4.	4dm by 3·5dm	**5.**	6m by 5·5m	**6.**	7·2mm by 5mm
7.	8m by 4½m	**8.**	12dm by 5¼dm	**9.**	10dam by $3\frac{1}{5}$dam
10.	5·4cm by 3·2cm	**11.**	6·4m by 4·5m	**12.**	8·2dm by 5·6dm
13.	2½km by $1\frac{3}{5}$km	**14.**	3¾m by $1\frac{1}{3}$m	**15.**	$3\frac{3}{5}$cm by $3\frac{1}{3}$cm

Volumes of cuboids (box shapes)

Exercise 20

Given the **length, breadth** and **height** find the **volumes** of the following cuboids:

1. 4cm by 3cm by 2cm
2. 6mm by 8mm by 8mm
3. 8m by 4m by 2½m
4. 10dm by 4½dm by 3dm
5. 7½cm by 4cm by 5cm
6. 8½m by 6½m by 4m
7. 5·4dm by 3·5dm by 2dm
8. 6·5cm by 4cm by 1·2cm
9. 8mm by 14·5mm by 3mm
10. 4·6m by 3·5m by 4m
11. 0·4km by 0·05km by 100km
12. 10dm by 6·8dm by 5·5dm

The calendar (not leap years)

Exercise 21

How many days in each of the following months?

1.	January	**2.**	March	**3.**	May	**4.**	July
5.	September	**6.**	November	**7.**	February	**8.**	April
9.	June	**10.**	August	**11.**	October	**12.**	December

How many days are there in the following periods? Include the first and last dates.

13. 20th Jan to 5th Mar
14. 15th Feb to 25th April
15. 10th Mar to 18th May
16. 5th April to 12th June
17. 8th May to 20th July
18. 16th June to 14th Sept
19. 4th Sept to 3rd Oct
20. 22nd Oct to 31st Dec

3 Revision exercises - algebra

Collecting like terms

Exercise 22

Collect like terms:

1.	a + a + a + a	**2.**	a + 2a + 3a + 4a
3.	2b + 4b + 6b + 8b	**4.**	3b + 5b + 7b + 9b
5.	a + b + a + b + a + b	**6.**	2a + b + 2a + b + 2a + b
7.	a + b + c + a + b + c	**8.**	a + 2b + 3c + a + 2b + 3c
9.	4c + 3c + 3b + 2b + 3a + 2a	**10.**	5b + 2c + a + 4c + 6a + b
11.	10a − 5a	**12.**	16a − 12a
13.	8a − 2a − 4a	**14.**	12a − 6a − 3a
15.	4a − 3a + 2a	**16.**	5a − 2a + 3a
17.	6a + 2a − 5a	**18.**	7a + 3a − 6a
19.	6a + 6b + 6c − 4c − 4b − 4c	**20.**	7a − 5c − 5b − 5a + 7c + 7b
21.	5a + 3b + c + c − 3b − 5a	**22.**	4a − 4a + 4b − 4b + 4c − 4c
23.	6a − 2b − 4c + 4b + 6c − a	**24.**	8c − 5a + 3b + 7a − b − 6c

Substitution

Exercise 23

If a = 8, b = 7, c = 6, d = 5, find the values of the following:

1.	a + b	**2.**	b − d	**3.**	2a − b	**4.**	3a + 3c
5.	2a − 2d	**6.**	2b + 2c	**7.**	6d − 2a	**8.**	6d + 2b
9.	2c − d	**10.**	9a + 9b	**11.**	4b − 3a	**12.**	7a + 7b
13.	7d + 2a	**14.**	8d − 2a	**15.**	3b + 6d	**16.**	12a − 12b

If a = 12, b = 11, c = 10, d = 9, find the values of the following:

17.	b + d	**18.**	a − d	**19.**	b − c	**20.**	c + d
21.	2a − b	**22.**	2a + 2c	**23.**	4d − 2a	**24.**	5d + 2a
25.	3a − 2d	**26.**	6d + 2a	**27.**	8d − 3a	**28.**	2b + c
29.	4b + 3a	**30.**	6a − 7d	**31.**	10a + 10b	**32.**	12a − 12b

Equations

Exercise 24

Find the value of 'x' in the following:

1. $5x = 45$ 2. $7x = 7$ 3. $4x = 20$ 4. $3x = 18$
5. $8x = 40$ 6. $11x = 66$ 7. $6x = 72$ 8. $6x = 48$
9. $5x = 0$ 10. $9x = 54$ 11. $7x = 49$ 12. $12x = 84$
13. $9x = 27$ 14. $11x = 132$ 15. $12x = 72$ 16. $8x = 96$
17. $12x = 108$ 18. $9x = 0$ 19. $9x = 63$ 20. $4x = 36$
21. $11x = 121$ 22. $10x = 100$ 23. $8x = 88$ 24. $12x = 144$
25. $2x + 3x + x = 7 + 12 + 5$ 26. $4x + 3x + 2x = 120 - 12$
27. $9x - 8x + 7x = 10 + 20 + 34$ 28. $20x - 8x - 5x = 60 - 8 + 4$
29. $24x - 7x - 5x = 70 + 54 - 28$ 30. $15x - 20x + 11x = 20 - 36 + 25$

Powers – index numbers

Exercise 25

Simplify the following:

1. $x \times x \times x \times x$ 2. $3x \times 2x \times x$
3. $2x \times 2x \times 2x \times 2x$ 4. $3x \times 4x \times 5x$
5. $x^2 \times x^2 \times x^2$ 6. $x^2 \times x^3 \times x^4$
7. $4x \times 3x^2 \times 2x^3$ 8. $x \times 2x^2 \times 3x^3 \times 4x^4$
9. $2x^2 \times 4x^2 \times 6x^2$ 10. $3x \times 3x \times 3x$
11. $x^4 \div x$ 12. $x^3 \div x^2$ 13. $x^5 \div x^3$ 14. $8x^2 \div 2x$
15. $9x^3 \div 3x$ 16. $4x^4 \div 2x^2$ 17. $12x^5 \div 3x^2$ 18. $16x^4 \div 8x^3$
19. $18x^5 \div 3x^4$ 20. $24x^4 \div x^4$ 21. $10x^4 \div x^2$ 22. $6x^3 \div 6x^3$

Exercise 26

If $x = 2$, find the value of the following:

1. x^2 2. $3x^2$ 3. x^3 4. $2x^3$ 5. x^4

If $x = 3$, find the value of the following:

6. x^2 7. $2x^3$ 8. x^4 9. $3x^2$ 10. x^5

If $x = 5$, find the value of the following:

11. x^2 12. x^3 13. $3x^2$ 14. $4x^3$ 15. x^4

4 Buying from a catalogue

Many people find it convenient to select the items they wish to purchase by using a **Mail Order Catalogue.** When they have made their choice from the catalogue, details of each item are set down on an **Order Form.** The details include the **Reference Number** of the item, the **Description,** the **Price** and, in some cases, the colour and size – for example, when buying clothes. The completed Order Form is passed to an **Agent** (a representative of the Mail Order Firm) who sends it to the firm's **warehouse.** The Agent is also responsible for collecting payment for the goods and ensuring that the customer receives the correct items.

At the back of this book you will find a catalogue, though only a small one, containing details of clothing and household items. We shall use a very simple Order Form, ignoring details of size and colour.

EXAMPLE

Ref. No.	Number required	Price each	Total cost
CB2	1	£5.75	£5.75
CB9	1	£3.75	£3.75
CG5	1	£2.85	£2.85
CG14	6	12p	72p
		Total	£13.07

Exercise 27

Write out an order form for each of these groups of items and find the total cost for each order:

1. 1 of CB 1
2 of CB 11
6 of CB 14

2. 1 of CG 2
2 of CG 3
2 of CG 12

3. 1 of CB 8
1 of CG 10
1 of CM 9

4. 1 of CM 16
1 of CW 18
1 of CW 20

5. 1 of CB 5
1 of CG 8
1 of CW 9

6. 1 of CM 6
1 of CW 10
1 of CW 24

7. 1 of CB 12
1 of CM 18
1 of CW 21

8. 1 of CM 2
1 of CW 2
1 of CW 15

9. 1 of CB 9
1 of CG 11
1 of CM 14

10. 2 of CB 15
1 of CG 13
12 of CM 20

11. 1 of CW 3
1 of CW 4
1 of CW 12

12. 1 of CB 3
1 of CG 1
1 of CM 15

13. 1 of CM 5
1 of CM 13
1 of CW 6
1 of CW 17

14. 2 of CB 7
2 of CG 4
2 of CW 19
2 of CW 23

15. 1 of CB 2
1 of CB 16
1 of CG 9
6 of CG 14

16. 1 of CM 3
2 of CM 8
1 of CM 10
1 of CM 12

17. 1 of CW 1
1 of CW 7
1 of CW 11
1 of CW 14

18. 1 of CB 4
1 of CG 6
1 of CM 1
6 of CW 22

19. 1 of CM 4
2 of CM 17
2 of CW 8
2 of CW 16

20. 1 of CB 6
2 of CB 10
2 of CG 7
1 of CM 19

21. 1 of CB 13
2 of CG 5
2 of CM 7
1 of CW 5

22. 1 of F3
1 of F 7
1 of F 10
1 of F 18

23. 1 of F 5
1 of F 6
1 of F 15
1 of HW 1

24. 1 of F 1
1 of HW 3
1 of HW 6
1 of HW 9

25. 1 of F 2
8m of F 16
1 of HW 14
1 of HW 22

26. 1 of F 4
2 of F 13
1 of HW 5
1 of L 6

27. 1 of F 9
1 of F 14
1 of HW 2
1 of HW 13

8. 1 of F 11
1 of F 12
1 of HW 10
1 of HW 17

29. 1 of F 8
6m of F 17
10 of L 3
1 of L 5

30. 1 of HW 4
1 of HW 11
1 of HW 18
1 of HW 19

How much change would you get from £100 if you placed any of the following orders? (questions 31 to 35)

31. 1 of L 7

32. 1 of HW 15
1 of HW 23

33. 1 of HW 20
1 of L 4

34. 1 of HW 7
1 of HW 12
1 of L 8

35. One of each of the following:
HW 8, HW 16, HW 21, L 1, L 2, L 9, L 10.

36 If you won a Premium Bond Prize for £100 how much more money would you need to buy item HW 24?
37 How many of item CM 11 can be bought for £130?
38 How many of item CW 13 can be bought for £310?
39 Item F 5 consists of four chairs. Find the cost of one chair.
40 How many metres of item F 16 can be bought for £41.25?

5 Averages

An average is found by adding together a group of separate values and dividing by their number.

EXAMPLE Find the average of 19·2, 16·3, 20·5, 11·6, 17·4

19·2
16·3
20·5
11·6
17·4
―――
85·0

$$\text{Average} = \frac{\text{Total value}}{\text{Number of items}}$$

$$= \frac{85}{5}$$

$$\text{Ans} = 17$$

Exercise 28

Find the average of:

1. 2, 4, 6, 8, 10, 12, 14, 16, 18, 20
2. 1, 2, 3, 4, 5, 6, 7, 8, 9, 10
3. 3, 6, 9, 12, 15, 18, 21, 24, 27
4. 5, 10, 15, 20, 25, 30, 35
5. 4, 14, 24, 34, 44, 54, 64
6. 37, 43, 57, 68, 72, 89
7. 211, 273, 327, 358, 434, 485
8. 2·73, 1·07, 3·59, 4·6, 0·96
9. 2·09m, 2·162m, 2·27m, 2·086m
10. £2.50, £3.83, £1.98, £4.25, £5.29
11. 35g, 136g, 26g, 82g, 76g
12. 3·5km, 0·79km, 2·01km, 4·62km
13. $7\frac{3}{4}$, $5\frac{1}{2}$, $3\frac{2}{3}$, $2\frac{1}{4}$, $4\frac{1}{3}$, $\frac{1}{2}$
14. 69p, £0.95, £1.51, 107p, £1.48
15. 3 at £3, 3 at £4.50, 3 at £6
16. 3 at £2.50, 4 at £3.50, 3 at £4.50
17. 1 at 3·98m, 2 at 4·34m, 3 at 4·57m, 4 at 4·75m
18. Catalogue items CB 13, CG 13, CM 19, CW 23
19. Catalogue items CB 6, CG 9, CM 5, CM 6
20. Catalogue items CB 8, CG 10, CM 9, CM 10, CM 11, CW 11, CW 12

6 Geometry

The quadrilateral

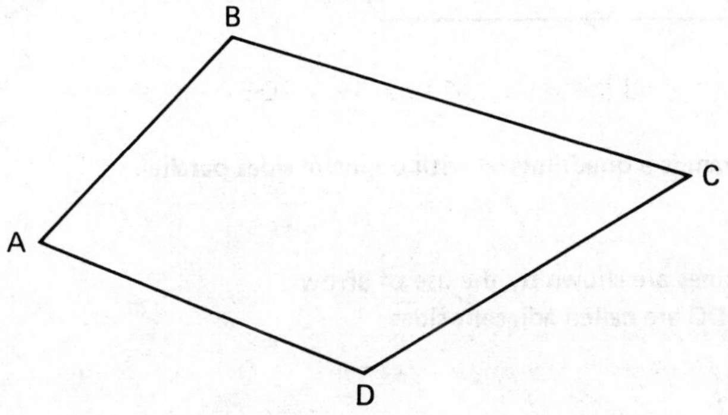

A quadrilateral is a plane (flat) figure with four straight sides.

Exercise 29

1 Draw quadrilateral ABCD in which AB = 4cm, AD = 5cm, CD = 6cm and BC = 7cm.

2 Use your protractor to measure ∠A, ∠B, ∠C and ∠D. Make a note of the values and add them together. What is the total?

3 Draw diagonal AC. Does AC bisect ∠DAB or ∠BCD? Check by measuring ∠BAC, ∠DAC and ∠BCA, ∠DCA.

4 Draw diagonal BD. Does BD bisect ∠ABC or ∠ADC? Check by measuring ∠ABD, ∠CBD and ∠ADB, ∠CDB.

5 Does diagonal AC **bisect** (cut in half) diagonal BD? Does diagonal BD bisect diagonal AC? Does AC = BD?

6 Let the point where AC cuts BD be called X. Measure ∠AXB, ∠BXC, ∠CXD, ∠DXA. Do the diagonals **intersect** (cut each other) at right-angles?

7 Add together the four angles at X. What is the total of these four angles?

8 Draw quadrilateral ABCD in which ∠A = 60°, ∠B = 80°, ∠C = 100°, ∠D = 120°.

9 Measure sides AB, BC. CD, DA as accurately as possible in centimetres (using decimal fractions).

10 Repeat the work of questions 2 to 7.

The parallelogram

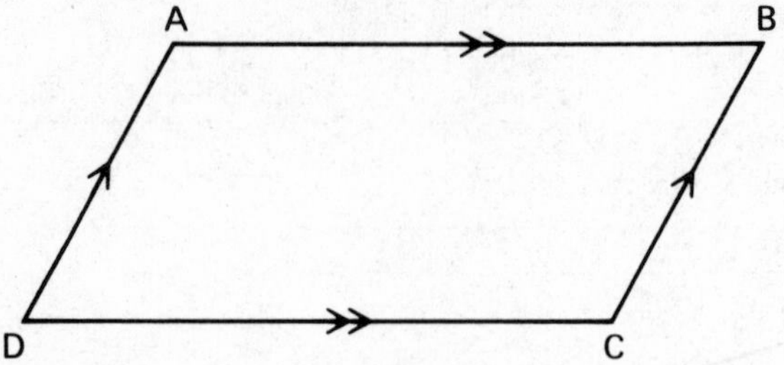

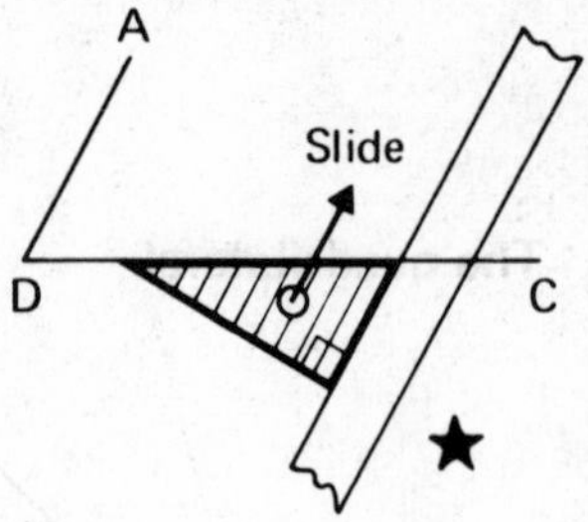

A parallelogram is a quadrilateral with opposite sides parallel.

NOTE
1 Parallel lines are shown by the use of arrows.
2 AD and DC are called **adjacent** sides.

Exercise 30

1 Draw parallelogram ABCD by the following steps:
(A) draw DC 7 cm long,
(B) construct ∠ADC equal to 60° and AD = 5cm,
(C) draw AB parallel to DC,
(D) draw CB parallel to DA.
★ The small sketch should remind you of the method of drawing parallel lines by using a set-square.
2 Measure AB and compare its length with DC.
3 Measure BC and compare its length with AD.
4 Measure ∠ABC and compare it with ∠ADC.
5 Measure ∠DAB and ∠BCD; compare them.
6 What is the sum (adding) of ∠CDA and ∠DAB?
7 What is the sum of ∠A, ∠B, ∠C, ∠D?
8 Draw diagonals AC and BD. Does AC = BD?
9 Does AC bisect either ∠BAD or ∠BCD?
10 Does BD bisect either ∠ADC or ∠ABC?
11 If AC and BD intersect at X, measure AX, CX and BX, DX. Do the diagonals bisect each other?
12 Measure the four angles at X. What is their sum?
13 Construct parallelogram ABCD in which DC = 8cm, AD = 6cm and ∠ADC = 70°. Repeat questions 2 to 12
14 Repeat questions 2 to 12 with a parallelogram of your own choice.

The rhombus

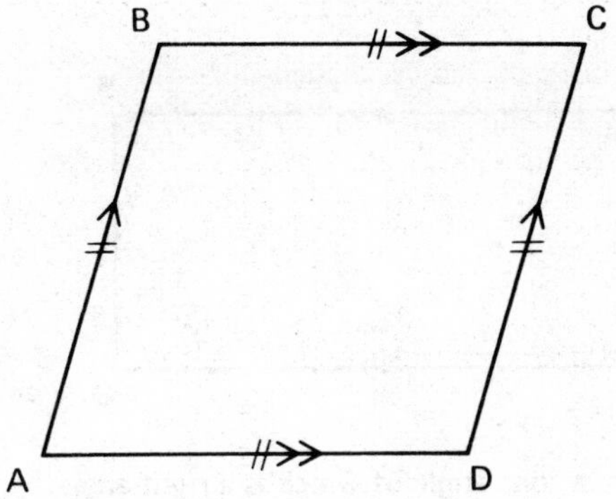

A rhombus is a parallelogram with adjacent sides equal.

Exercise 31

1 Parallelograms were used in Exercise 29. In these parallelograms were the *'adjacent sides equal'*? Note the important difference between an ordinary parallelogram and a rhombus.

2 Draw rhombus ABCD by the following steps:
(A) draw AD 6cm long,
(B) construct ∠DAB equal to 65° and AB = 6cm,
(C) draw BC || AD,
NOTE. The abbreviation for 'parallel to' is || .
(D) draw CD || AB.

3 Measure BC and compare its length with AD.

4 Measure CD and compare its length with AB.

5 Measure ∠BCD and compare it with ∠DAB.

6 Measure ∠ABC and ∠ADC; compare them.

7 What is the sum of ∠DAB and ∠ABC?

8 What is the sum of ∠A, ∠B, ∠C, ∠D?

9 Draw diagonals AC and BD. Does AC = BD?

10 Does AC bisect either ∠BAD or ∠BCD?

11 Does BD bisect either ∠ABC or ∠ADC?

12 If AC and BD intersect at X, measure AX, CX and BX, DX. Do the diagonals bisect each other?

13 Measure the four angles at X. What do you notice? What is the sum of the four angles?

14 Repeat questions 3 to 13 with a rhombus of your own choice.

The rectangle

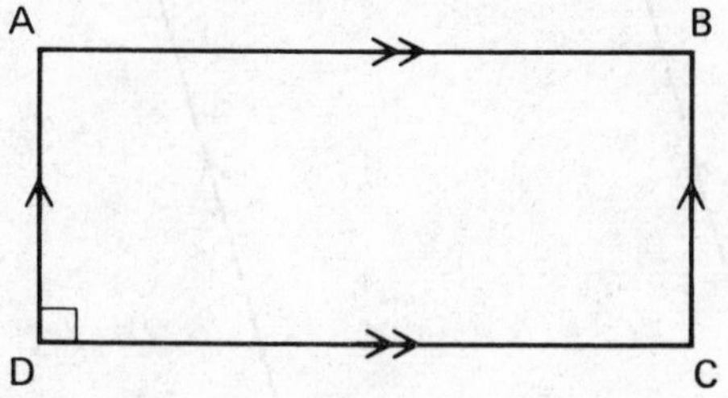

A rectangle is a parallelogram, one angle of which is a right-angle.

Exercise 32

1 Draw rectangle ABCD by the following steps:
 (A) draw DC 8cm long,
 (B) construct $\angle CDA$ equal to 90° and AD = 5cm,
 (C) draw AB || DC,
 (D) draw BC || AD.

2 Measure AB and compare its length with DC.

3 Measure BC and compare its length with AD.

4 Measure $\angle A$, $\angle B$, $\angle C$. Compare them with $\angle D$.

5 What is the sum of $\angle D$ and $\angle A$?

6 What is the sum of $\angle A$, $\angle B$, $\angle C$, $\angle D$?

7 Draw the diagonals AC and BD. Does AC = BD?

8 Does AC bisect either $\angle BAD$ or $\angle BCD$?

9 Does BD bisect either $\angle ADC$ or $\angle ABC$?

10 If AC and BD intersect at X, measure AX, CX and BX, DX. Do the diagonals bisect each other?

11 Measure the four angles at X. What is their sum?

12 What is the area of rectangle ABCD?

13 What do you think the area of ΔABD will be? And ΔBCD? And ΔACD? And ΔACB?

14 What is your guess for the areas of the triangles AXB, BXC, CXD, DXA?

15 Repeat questions 2 to 14 with a rectangle measuring 10cm by 4cm.

The square

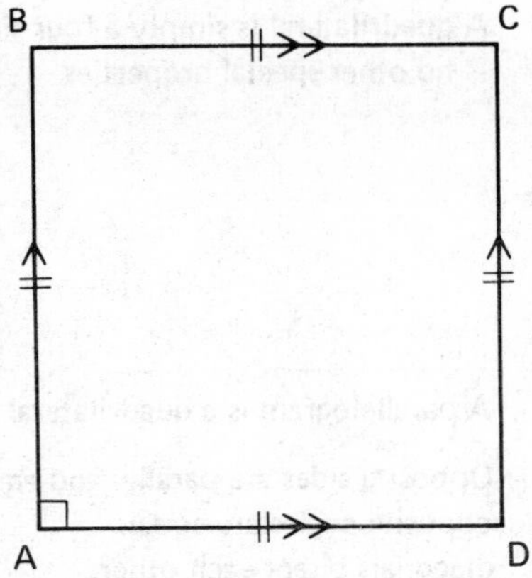

A square is a rectangle in which the adjacent sides are equal.

Exercise 33

1 Draw square ABCD by the following steps:
(A) draw AD 6cm long,
(B) construct ∠DAB equal to 90° and AB = 6cm,
(C) draw BC || AD,
(D) draw CD || AB.
2 Measure BC and compare its length with AD.
3 Measure CD and compare its length with AB.
4 Measure ∠B, ∠C, ∠D. Compare them with ∠A.
5 What is the sum of ∠A and ∠B?
6 What is the sum of ∠A, ∠B, ∠C, ∠D?
7 Draw the diagonals AC and BD. Does AC = BD?
8 Does AC bisect either ∠BAD or ∠BCD?
9 Does BD bisect either ∠ABC or ∠ADC?
10 What is the size of ∠BAC, ∠DAC, ∠BCA, ∠DCA, ∠ABD, ∠CBD, ∠ADB, ∠CDB?
11 If AC and BD intersect at X, measure AC, CX and BX, DX. Do the diagonals bisect each other?
12 Measure the four angles at X. What do you notice? What is the sum of the four angles?
13 What is the area of square ABCD?
14 What do you think the area of △ABC will be? And △ADC? And △DAB? And △CBD?
15 What is your guess for the areas of the triangles AXB, AXD, CXB, CXD?
16 Repeat questions 2 to 15 with a square measuring 8cm by 8cm.

Things to remember

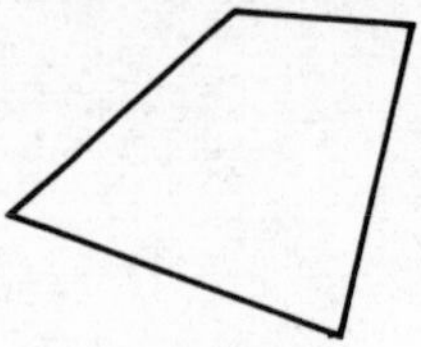

quadrilateral

A quadrilateral is simply a four-sided plane figure – no other special properties.

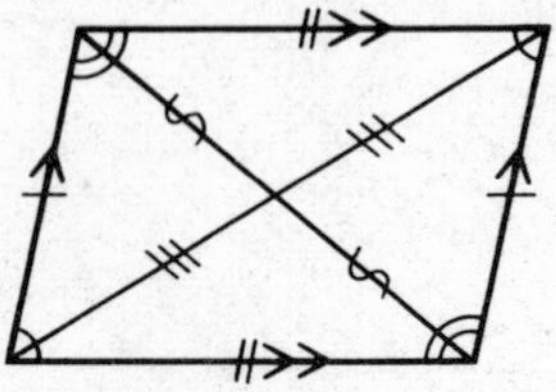

parallelogram

A parallelogram is a quadrilateral so it has four sides.

Opposite sides are parallel and equal;
opposite angles are equal;
diagonals bisect each other.

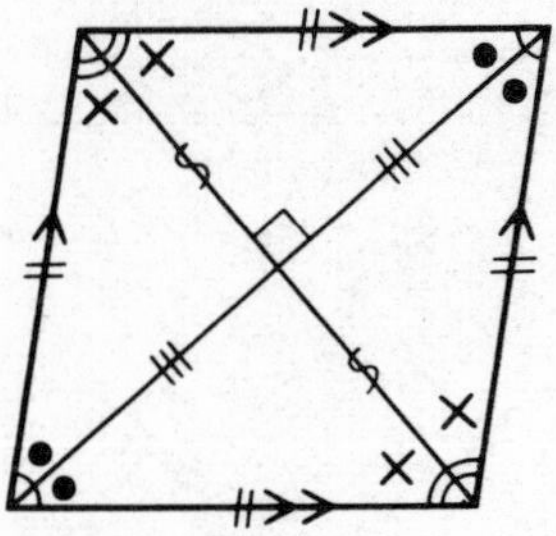

rhombus

A rhombus is a parallelogram so it has four sides; opposite sides are parallel and equal, opposite angles are equal and the diagonals bisect each other.

The diagonals bisect the interior angles of the rhombus;
the diagonals bisect each other at right angles;
adjacent sides are equal.

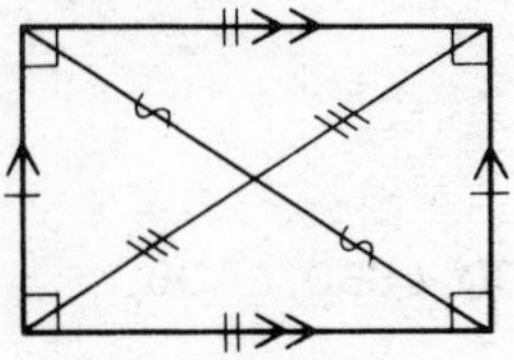

rectangle

A rectangle is a parallelogram so it has four sides; opposite sides are parallel and equal, opposite angles are equal and the diagonals bisect each other.

The diagonals are equal in length;
the interior angles are right-angles.

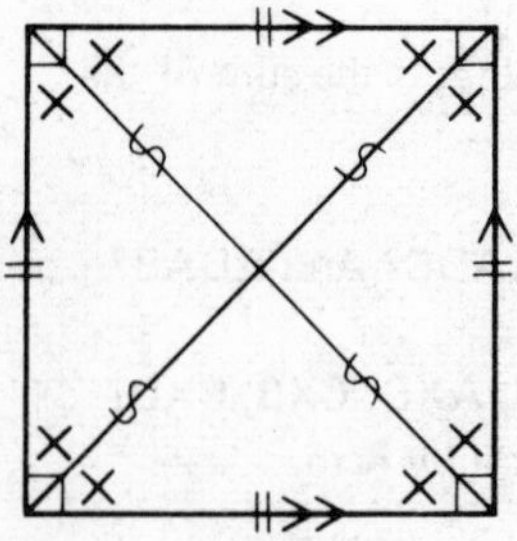

square

A square is a rectangle so it has four sides; opposite sides are parallel and equal, the diagonals bisect each other and are equal in length, the interior angles are right angles.

The diagonals bisect the interior angles of the square;
the diagonals bisect each other at right angles;
adjacent sides are equal.

7 Area

Areas of rectangles by subtraction

EXAMPLE A rectangular lawn, 50m long by 30m wide, is surrounded by a path 3m wide. Find the area of the path.

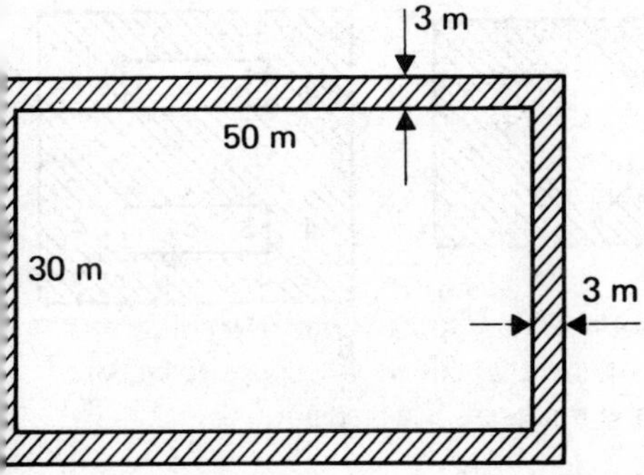

$$\begin{array}{r} 56 \times \\ 36 \\ \hline \\ \hline 2016 \\ \hline \end{array} \qquad \begin{array}{r} 50 \times \\ 30 \\ \hline \\ \hline 1500 \\ \hline \end{array}$$

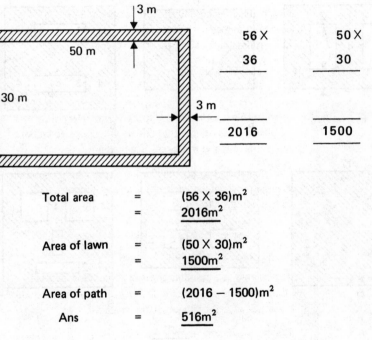

Total area = $(56 \times 36)m^2$
= $\underline{2016m^2}$

Area of lawn = $(50 \times 30)m^2$
= $\underline{1500m^2}$

Area of path = $(2016 - 1500)m^2$
Ans = $\underline{516m^2}$

QUESTION Why does the whole area measure 56m by 36m?

Exercise 34

Find the area of the shaded portion and the outside perimeter of the following. The dimensions are in metres.

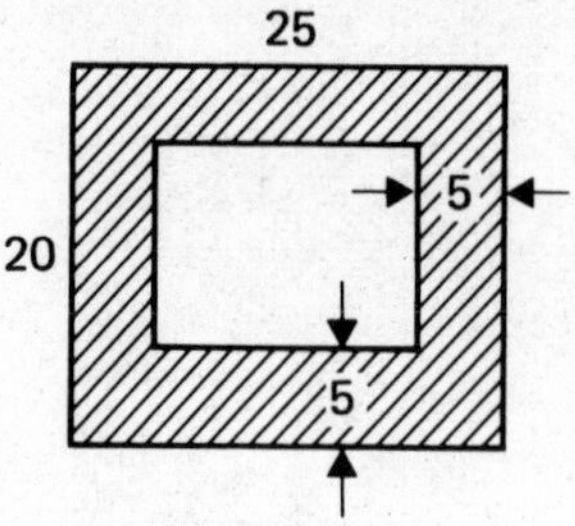

1

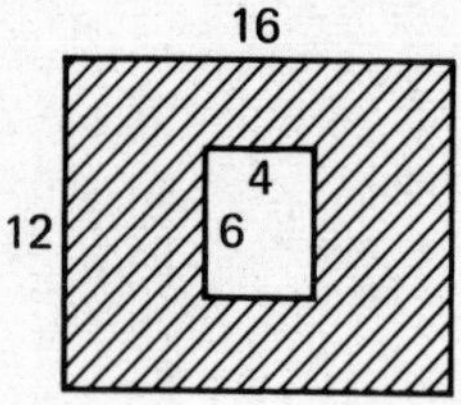

2

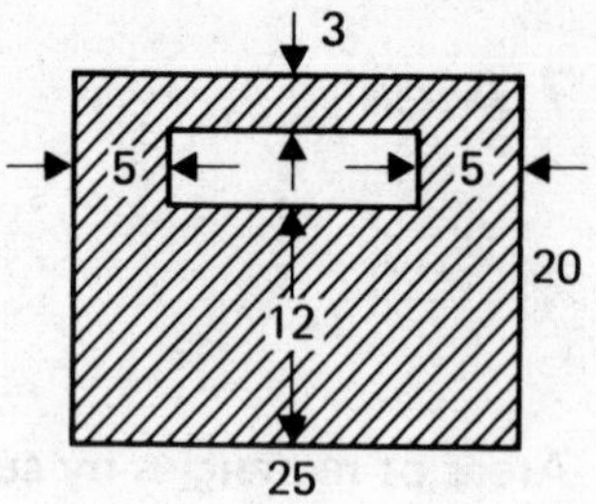

3

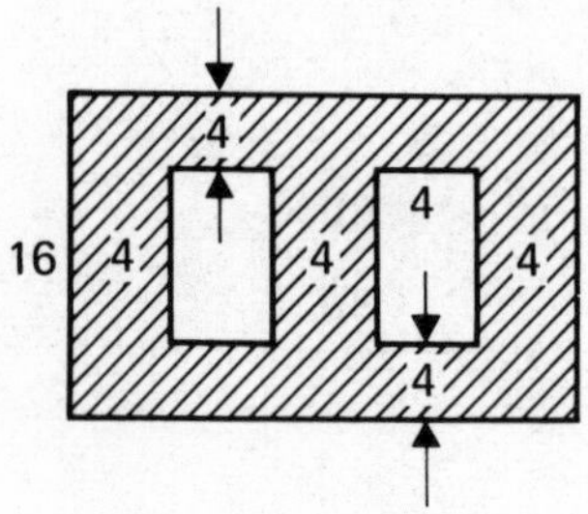

4

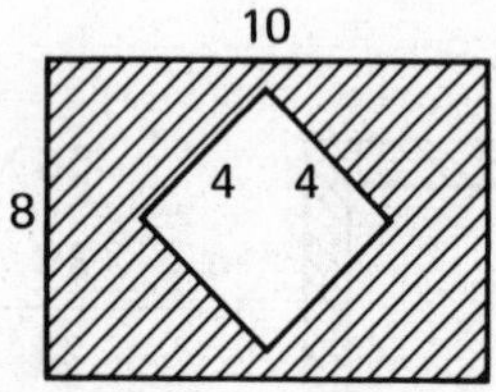

5

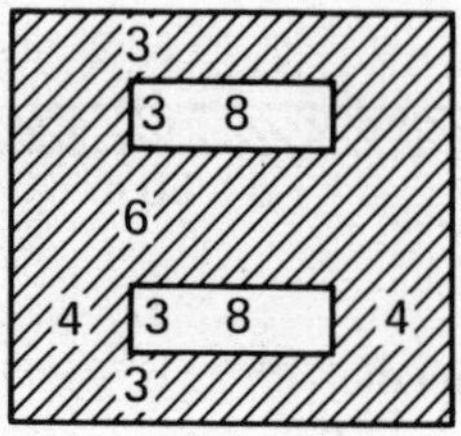

6

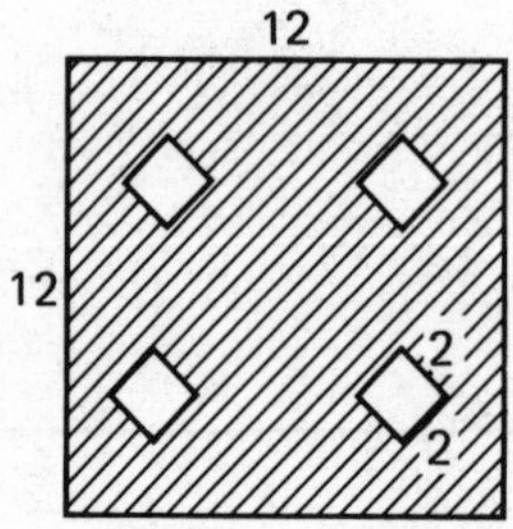

7

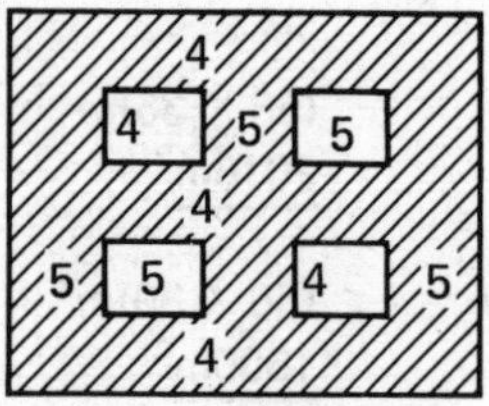

8

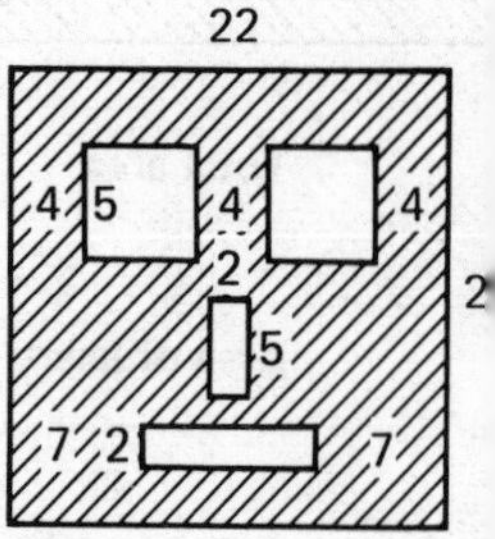

9

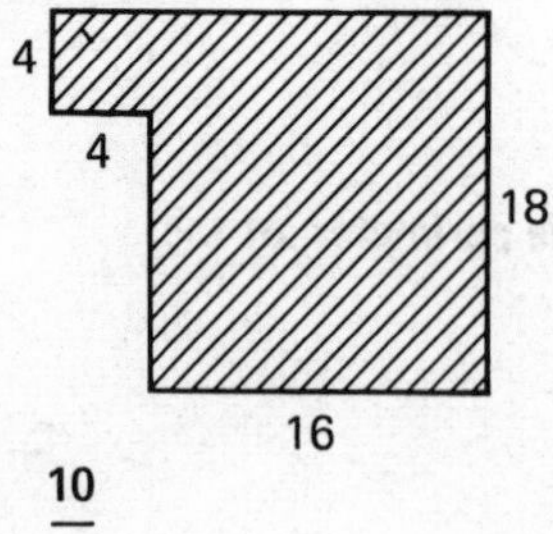

10

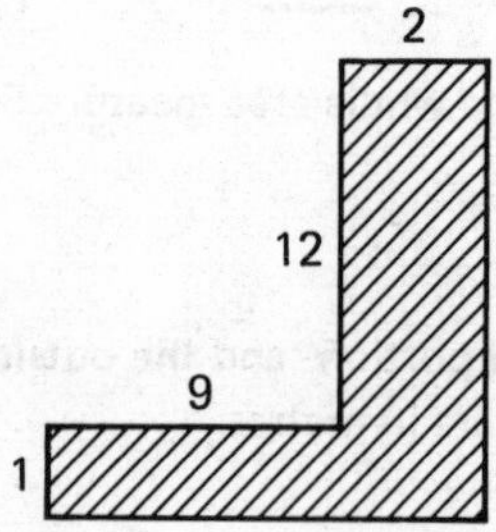

11

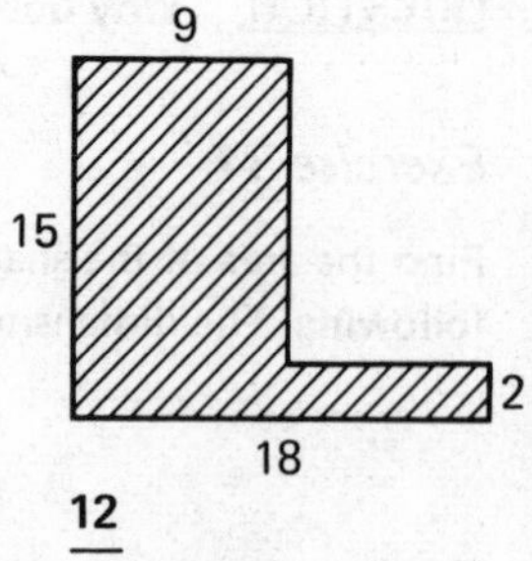

12

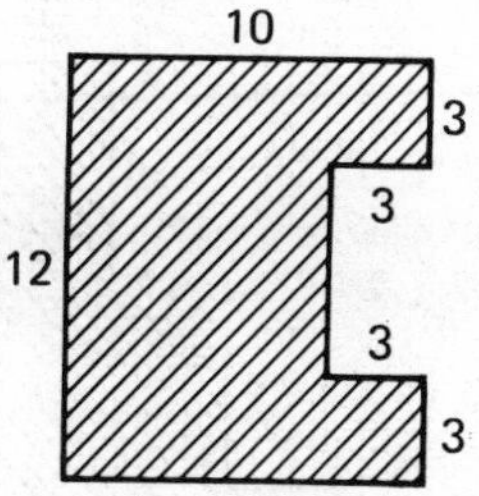

13

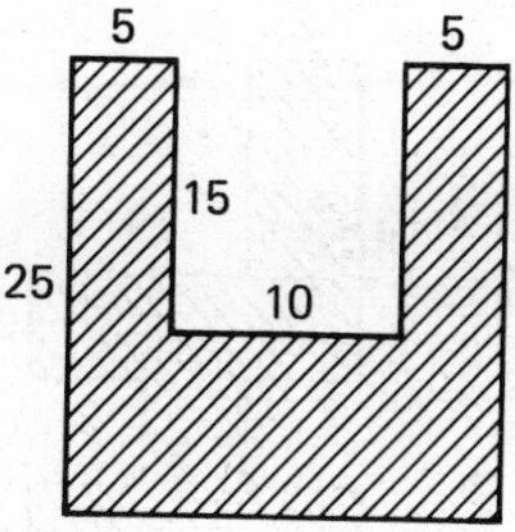

14

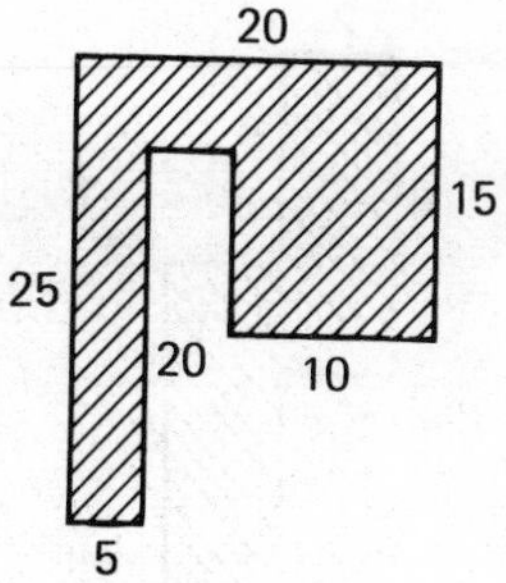

15

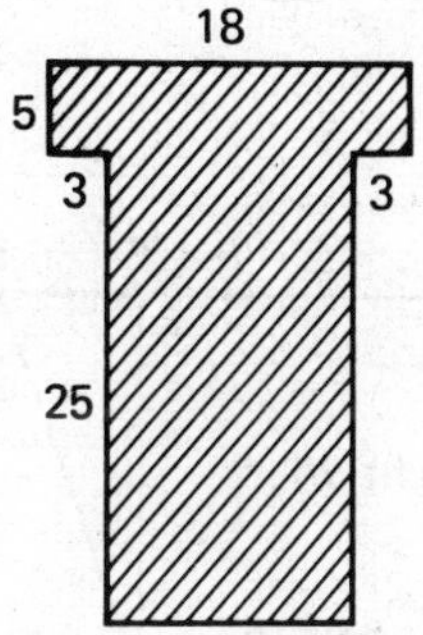

16

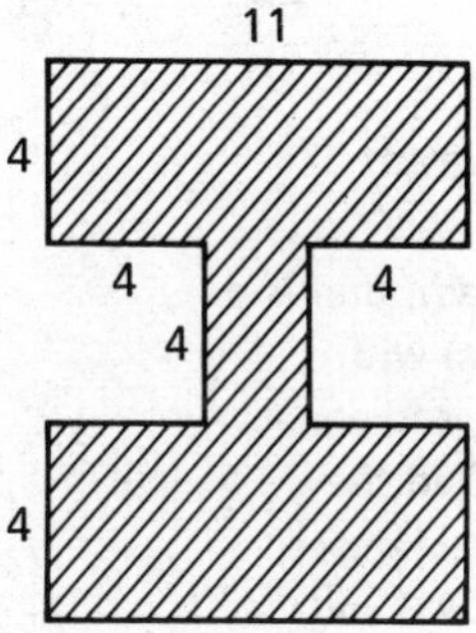

17

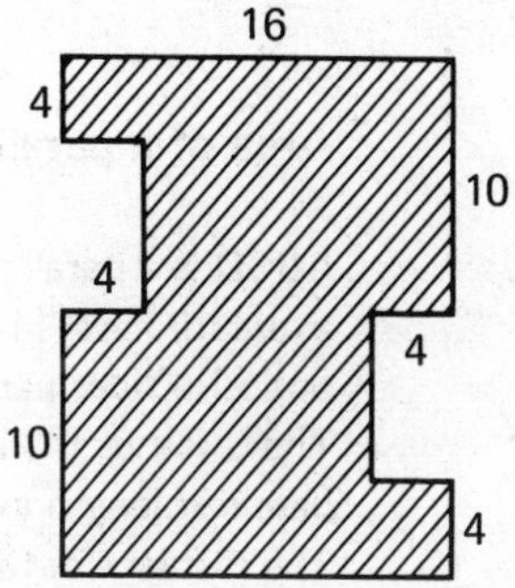

18

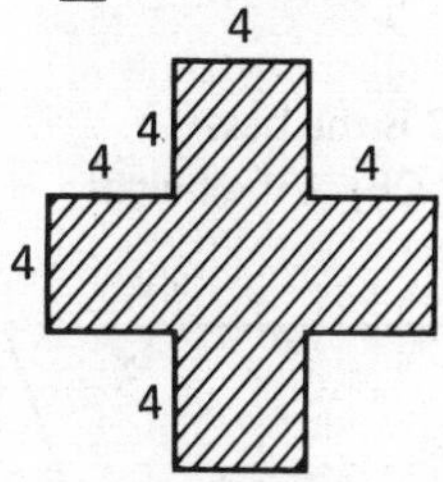

19

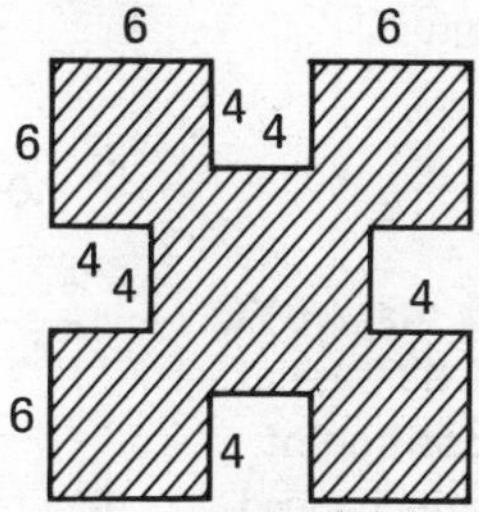

20

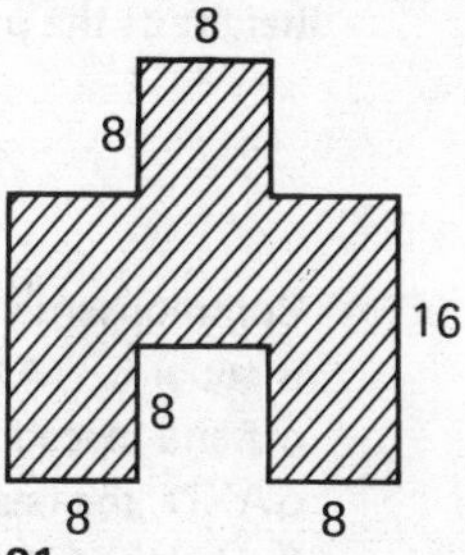

21

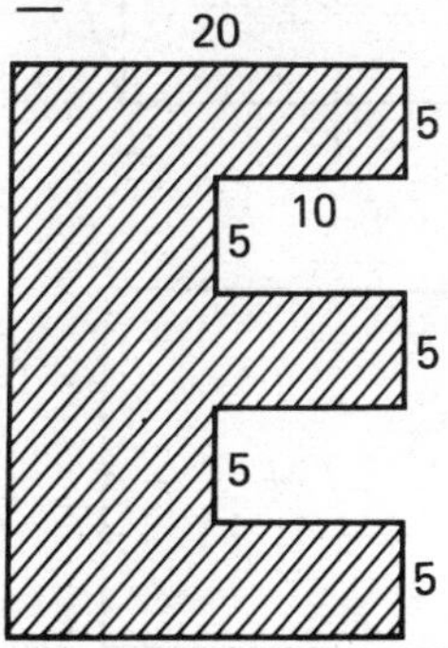

22

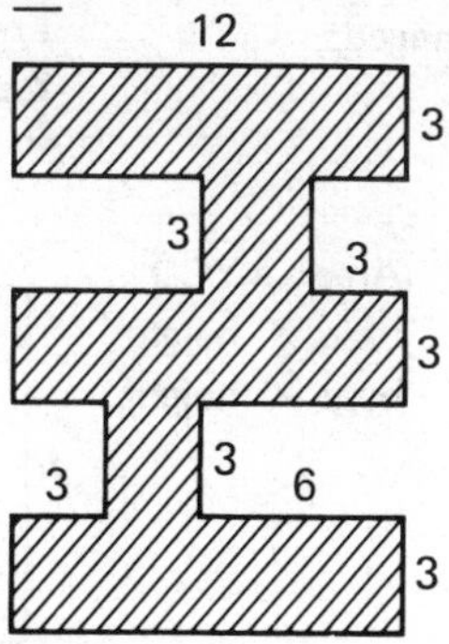

23

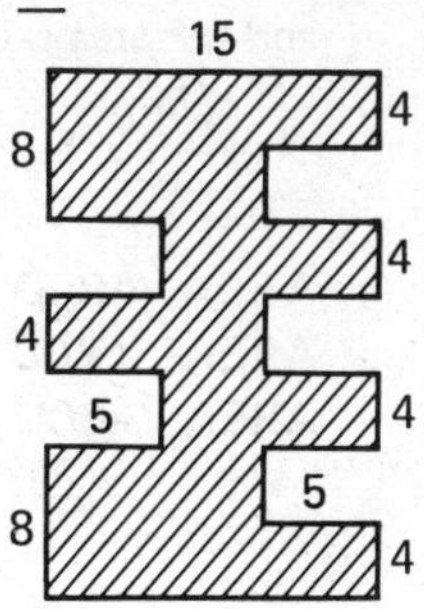

24

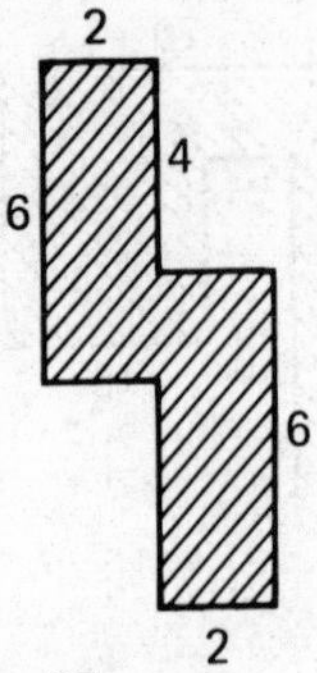

25

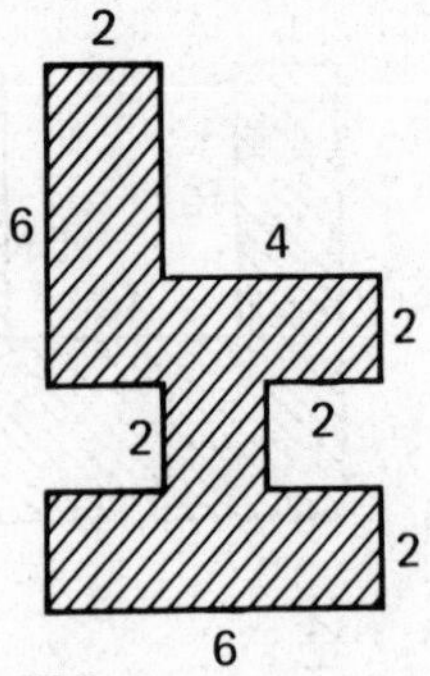

26

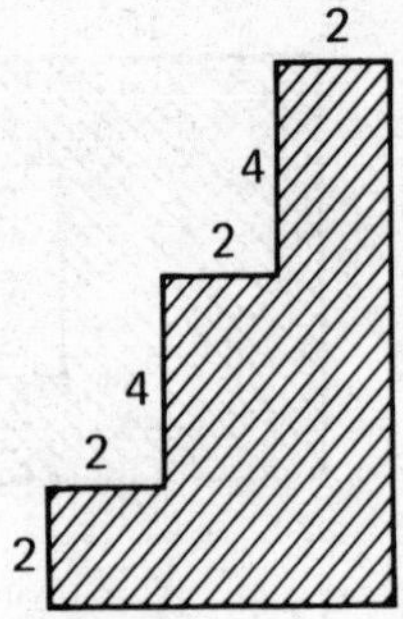

27

Area of a parallelogram

ABCD is a parallelogram, that is a quadrilateral (4 sides) with opposite sides parallel and equal. The distance DC is called the **base** not **length** as in rectangles. The distance between AB and CD is called the **perpendicular height** of the parallelogram.

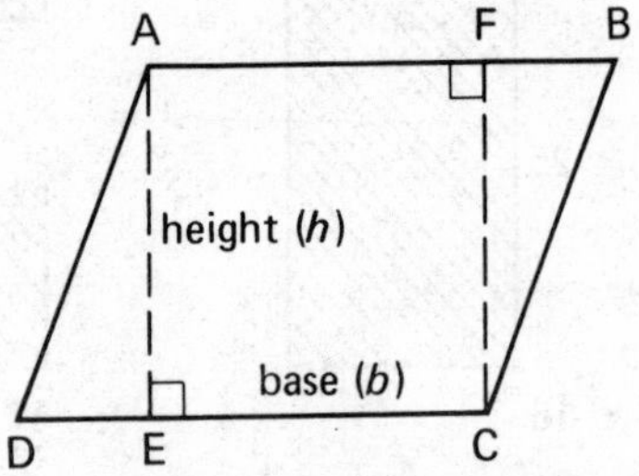

DC is the base
AE (and CF) is the height

Commonsense suggests that $\triangle BYC$ is equal to $\triangle AXD$. If $\triangle BYC$ is cut off and placed in the position of $\triangle AXD$, the base DC is unchanged, the height CY (and DX) is unchanged and the area is unchanged.

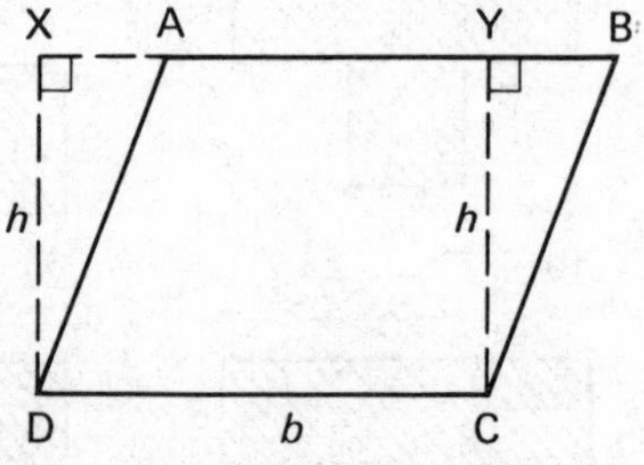

AREA ABCD = Area XYCD
AREA XYCD = base × height
AREA ABCD = base × height

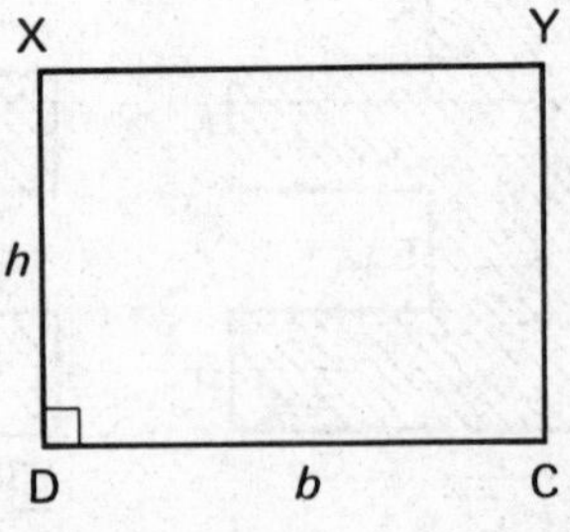

AREA OF PARALLELOGRAM = BASE $\times$ HEIGHT

We must understand that any side of a parallelogram may be regarded as the 'base'; in each case there will be a 'height' to go with it. Consider the next two diagrams.

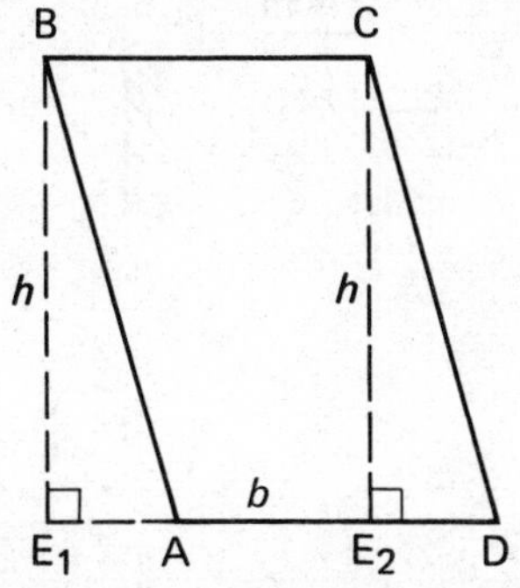

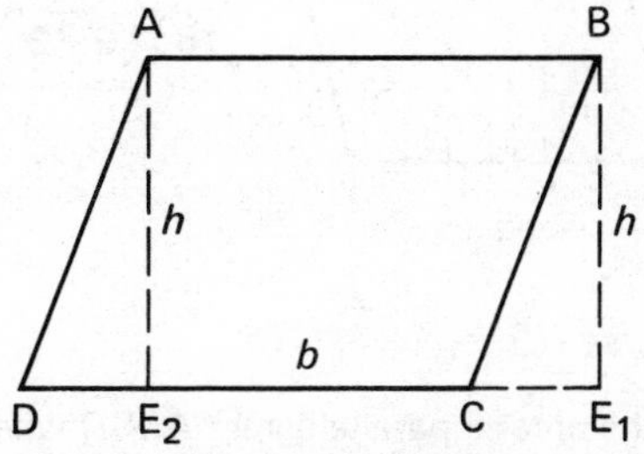

They show two different views of parallelogram ABCD with different bases and matching heights. Note the position of E_1, showing how the height may fall **outside** the base.

NOTE The abbreviation for parallelogram is $||^{gram}$

EXAMPLE 1 Find the area of a parallelogram ABCD whose base is 5cm and height 3cm.

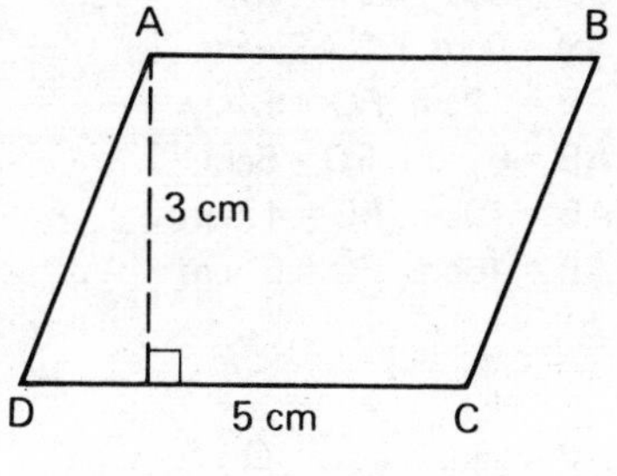

Area of $||^{gram}$ = base $\times$ height

= 5cm $\times$ 3cm

Ans = $15cm^2$

EXAMPLE 2 Find the area of a parallelogram PQRS whose base is $1\frac{1}{3}$ m and height $\frac{3}{4}$ m.

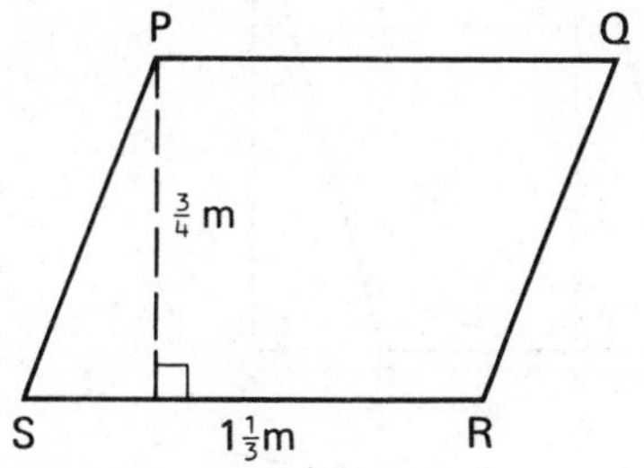

Area of $||^{gram}$ = base $\times$ height

= $1\frac{1}{3}$m $\times$ $\frac{3}{4}$m

= $\left(\frac{\cancel{4}^{1}}{\cancel{3}_{1}} \times \frac{\cancel{3}^{1}}{\cancel{4}_{1}}\right) m^2$

Ans = $1m^2$

EXAMPLE 3   The area of parallelogram WXYZ is $19{\cdot}2cm^2$ and the height is 8cm. Find the length of the base.

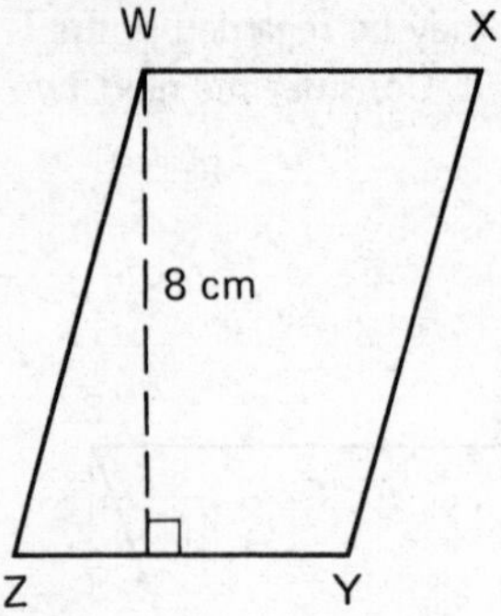

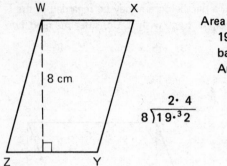

Area of $\|\|^{gram}$	=	base X height
$19{\cdot}2cm^2$	=	base X 8cm
base	=	$(19{\cdot}2 \div 8)$cm
Ans	=	2·4cm

$$\begin{array}{r} 2{\cdot}\ 4 \\ 8\overline{)1\,9{\cdot}{}^{3}2} \end{array}$$

Exercise 35

Find the area of parallelogram ABCD when:

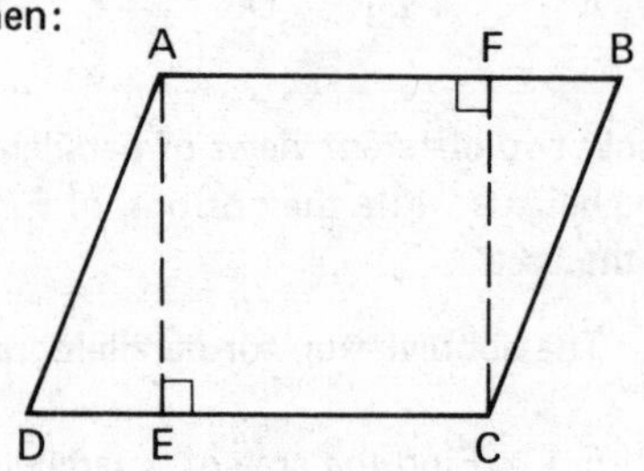

1. CD = 5cm, AE = 4cm
2. CD = 9cm, AE = 5cm
3. CD = 7cm, AE = 6cm
4. CD = 9cm, AE = 6cm
5. CD = 8cm, AE = 7cm
6. CD = 9cm, AE = 7cm
7. CD = 12cm, AE = 3cm
8. CD = 7cm, AE = 4cm
9. CD = 8cm, AE = 5cm
10. CD = 9cm, AE = 5cm
11. AB = 6½cm, FC = 4cm
12. AB = 8cm, FC = 2¼cm
13. AB = 4¼cm, FC = 4cm
14. AB = 12cm, FC = 6¼cm
15. AB = $5\frac{1}{3}$cm, FC = 3cm
16. AB = $6\frac{2}{3}$cm, FC = 6cm
17. AB = $7\frac{1}{5}$cm, FC = 5cm
18. AB = 10cm, FC = $4\frac{2}{5}$cm
19. AB = $6\frac{1}{8}$cm, FC = 4cm
20. AB = 16cm, FC = $5\frac{3}{8}$cm

Exercise 36

Find the area of parallelogram PQRS when:

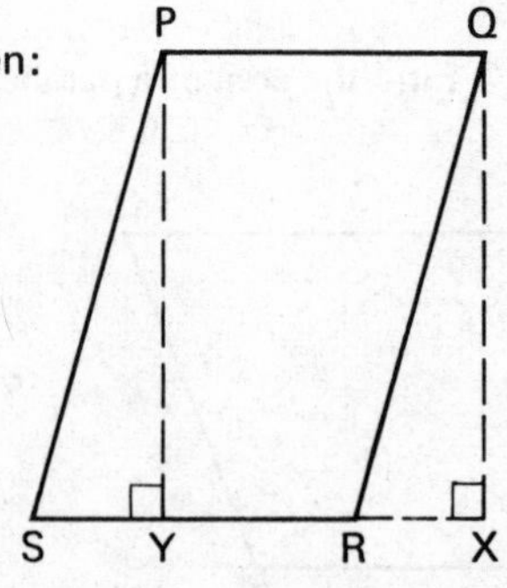

1. SR = 3·2cm, PY = 5cm
2. SR = 4·5cm, PY = 6cm
3. SR = 4cm, PY = 5·25cm
4. SR = 6·3cm, PY = 10cm
5. SR = 5cm, PY = 8·4cm
6. SR = 8cm, PY = 12·5cm
7. SR = 4·2cm, PY = 7cm
8. SR = 6·3cm, PY = 9cm

9. SR = 7cm, PY = 8·6cm
10. SR = 8·8cm, PY = 12cm
11. PQ = 3·2cm, PY = 6·3cm
12. PQ = 4·3cm, PY = 7·2cm
13. SR = 2·7cm, QX = 5·4cm
14. SR = 5·5cm, QX = 8·4cm
15. PQ = 4·6cm, QX = 6·8cm
16. PQ = 6·2cm, QX = 6·2cm
17. PQ = 1·8cm, QX = 2·7cm
18. PQ = 3·4cm, QX = 9·3cm
19. PQ = 2·34cm, QX = 1·2cm
20. PQ = 1·01cm, QX = 3·67cm
21. If the area = 3·64m^2 and PY = 2·6m, find PQ.
22. If the area = 16·1m^2 and QX = 4·6m, find SR.
23. If the area = 26·46m^2 and SR = 2·7m, find PY.
24. If the area = 16·128m^2 and PY = 3·84m, find PQ.
25. If the area = 31·808m^2 and SR = 5·6m, find QX.

Area of a triangle

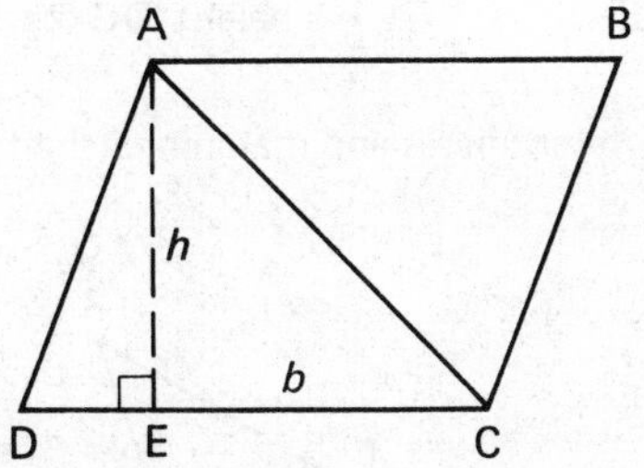

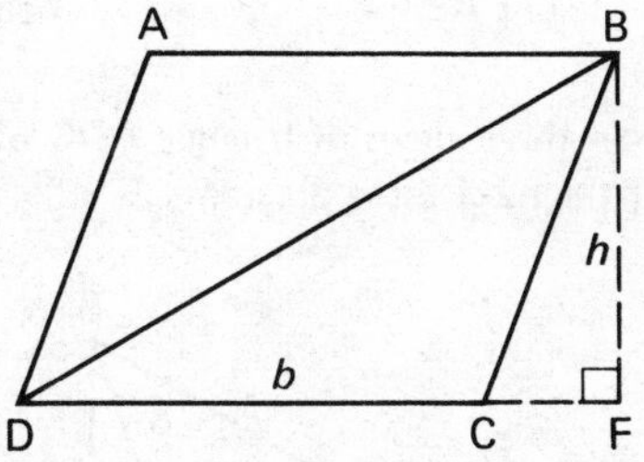

The diagonal of a parallelogram cuts the figure in half (*bisects it*); therefore, each of the triangles formed by the diagonal will have an area equal to half the area of the parallelogram.

Triangles ACD and BCD are equal in area because each is equal to half the area of ABCD.

The area of parallelogram ABCD is:

$$\text{base} \times \text{height}$$

The area of each triangle is half of ABCD

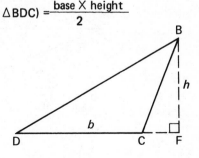

$$\text{Area of } \triangle ADC \text{ (and } \triangle BDC) = \frac{\text{base} \times \text{height}}{2}$$

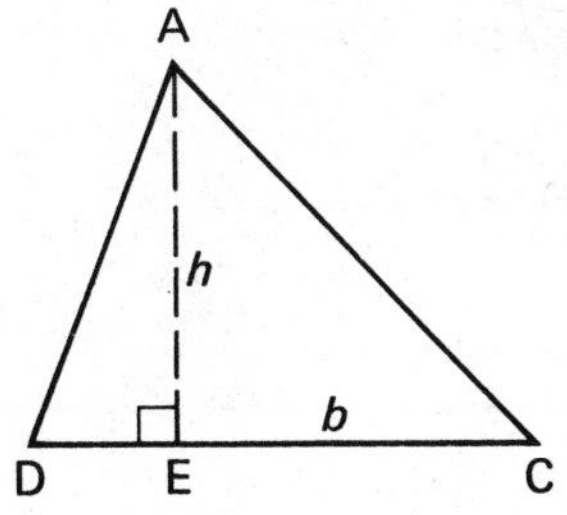

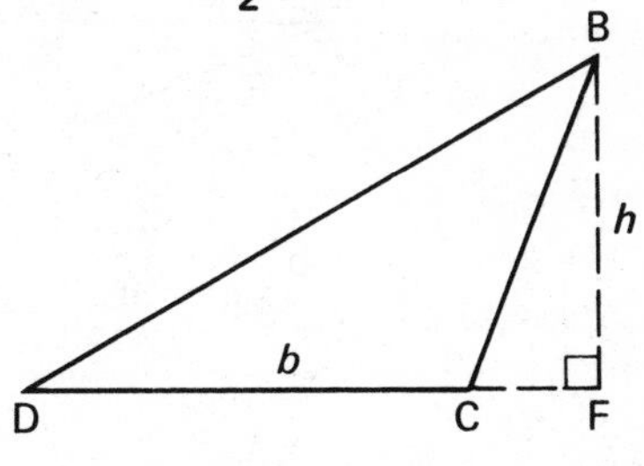

$$\text{AREA OF TRIANGLE} = \frac{\text{BASE} \times \text{HEIGHT}}{2}$$

We must understand that any side of a triangle may be regarded as the 'base'; in each case there will be a 'height' to go with it. Consider the next three diagrams.

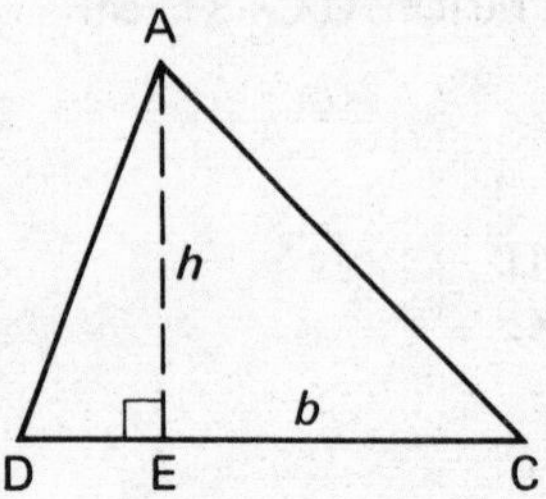

base CD
height AE

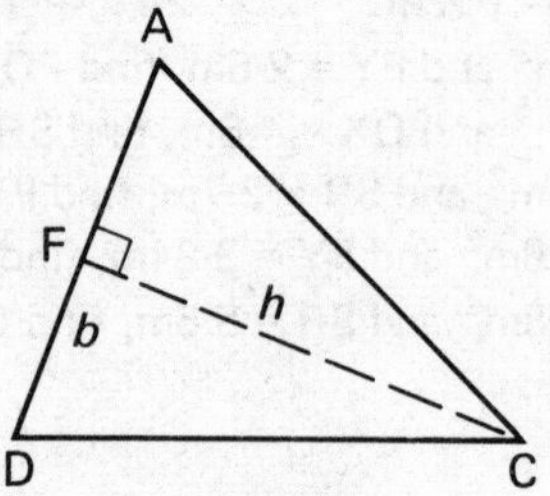

base AD
height CF

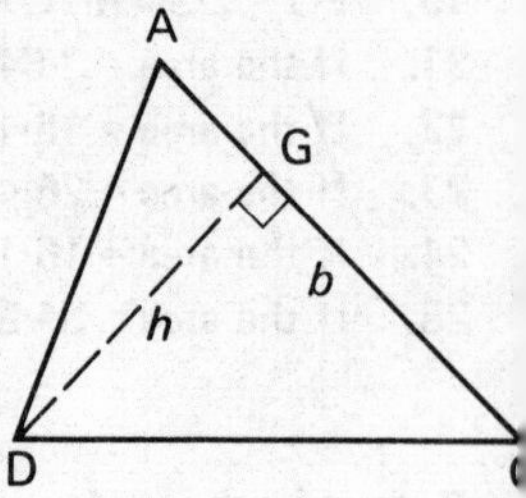

base AC
height DG

They show three views of triangle ADC with different bases and matching heights. Consider the next three diagrams.

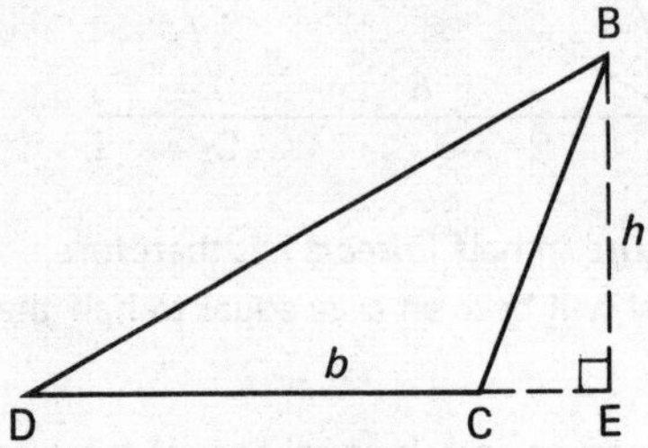

base CD
height BE

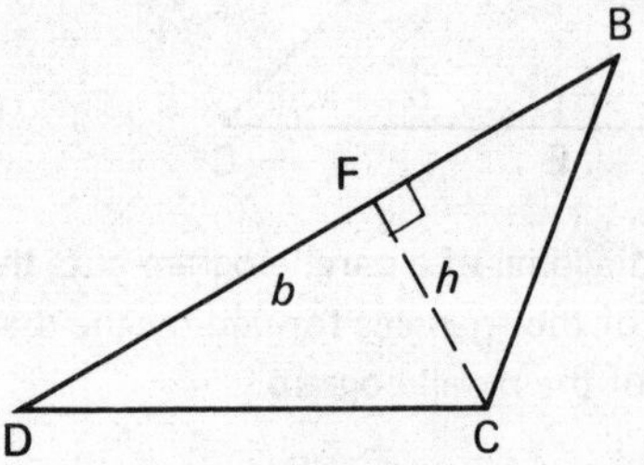

base BD
height CF

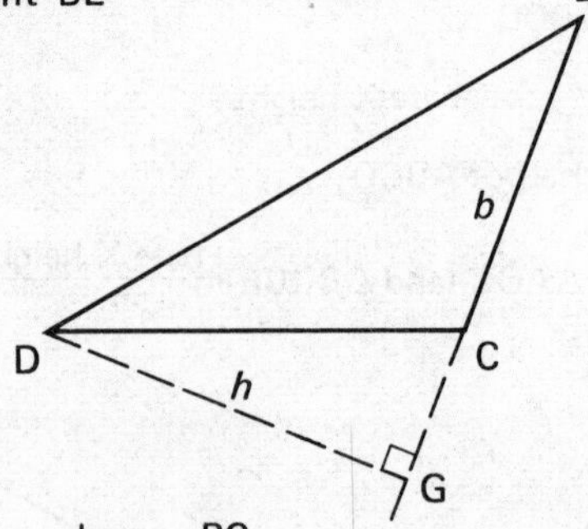

base BC
height DG

They show three views of triangle BCD with different bases and matching heights. Note the positions of E and G, showing how the height may fall **outside** the base.

EXAMPLE 1 Find the area of triangle ABC whose base is 6cm and height 4cm.

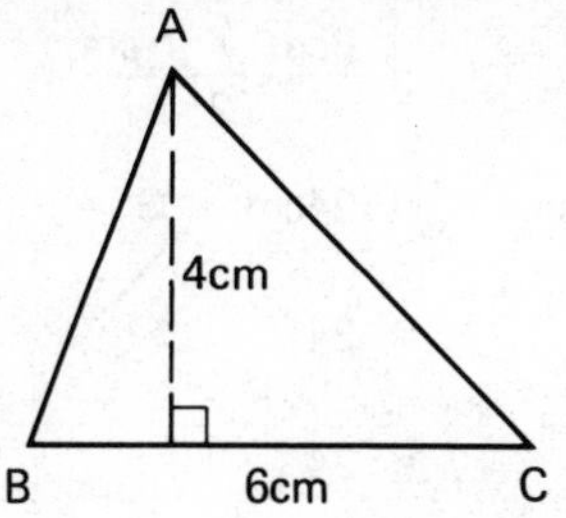

$$\text{Area of triangle} = \frac{\text{base} \times \text{height}}{2}$$

$$= \frac{6\text{cm} \times 4\text{cm}}{2}$$

$$= \frac{\cancel{24}^{\,12}}{\cancel{2}_{\,1}} \quad \bigstar$$

$$\text{Ans} = \underline{12\text{cm}^2}$$

NOTE ★ Cancelling may be carried out earlier

$$\frac{{}^{3}\cancel{6}\text{cm} \times 4\text{cm}}{\cancel{2}_{\,1}} \qquad \text{or} \qquad \frac{6\text{cm} \times {}^{2}\cancel{4}\text{cm}}{\cancel{2}_{\,1}}$$

$$\text{Ans} = \underline{12\text{cm}^2} \qquad\qquad \text{Ans} = \underline{12\text{cm}^2}$$

EXAMPLE 2 Find the area of a triangle XYZ whose base is $2\frac{2}{3}$m and height $8\frac{1}{4}$m.

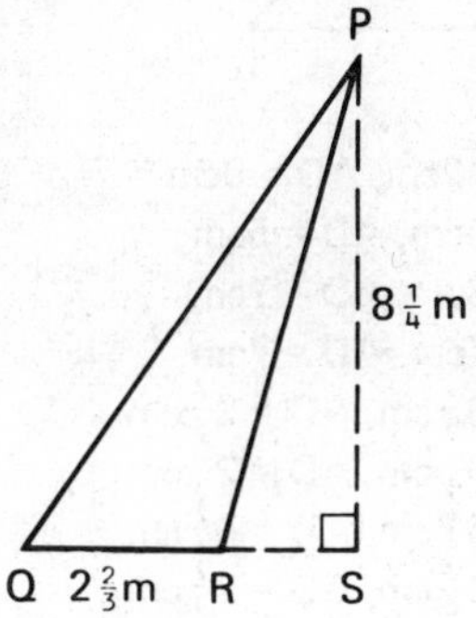

$$\text{Area of triangle} = \frac{\text{base} \times \text{height}}{2}$$

$$= \frac{2\frac{2}{3}\text{m} \times 8\frac{1}{4}\text{m}}{2}$$

$$\left(\frac{\cancel{8}^{\,2}}{\cancel{3}_{\,1}} \times \frac{\cancel{33}^{\,11}}{\cancel{4}_{\,1}} \times \frac{1}{2}\right)\text{m}^2 \;\bigstar$$

$$= \frac{\cancel{22}^{\,11}}{\cancel{2}_{\,1}}\ \text{m}^2$$

$$\text{Ans} = \underline{11\text{m}^2}$$

NOTE ★ Multiplying by ½ has the same result as dividing by 2.

The formula could be written as:

AREA OF TRIANGLE = ½ (BASE X HEIGHT)

EXAMPLE 3 If the area of a triangle is 24cm² and the base 6cm, find the height.

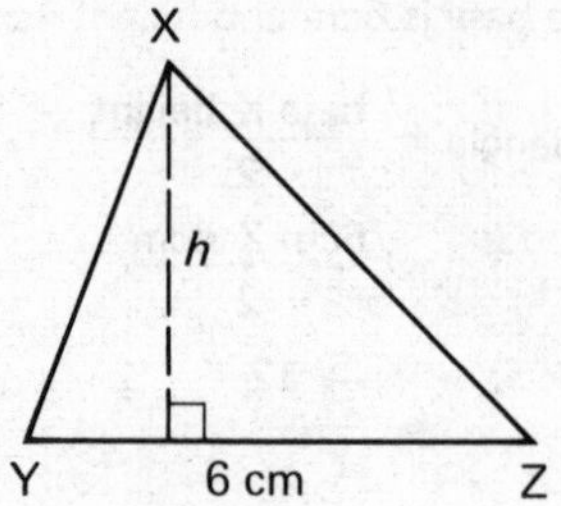

$$\text{Area of triangle} = \frac{\text{base} \times \text{height}}{2}$$

$$= \frac{6\text{cm} \times h\,\text{cm}}{2}$$

But the area $= 24\text{cm}^2$

$$\therefore \frac{\overset{3}{\cancel{6}} \times h}{\cancel{2}_1} = 24$$

$$3h = 24$$

$$h = 8$$

Ans = 8cm

Exercise 37

Find the area of triangle ABC when:

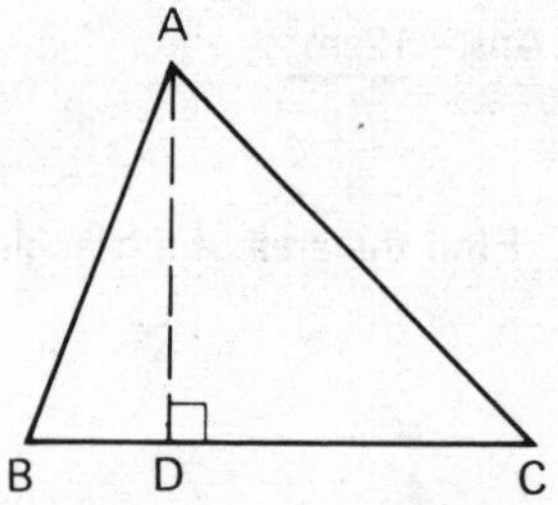

1. BC = 4cm, AD = 3cm
2. BC = 5cm, AD = 4cm
3. BC = 2cm, AD = 5cm
4. BC = 3cm, AD = 2cm
5. BC = 4cm, AD = 7cm
6. BC = 5cm, AD = 6cm
7. BC = 4cm, AD = 6cm
8. BC = 6cm, AD = 7cm
9. BC = 8cm, AD = 10cm
10. BC = 12cm, AD = 9cm
11. BC = 3cm, AD = 3cm
12. BC = 5cm, AD = 5cm
13. BC = 3cm, AD = 5cm
14. BC = 3cm, AD = 7cm
15. BC = 5cm, AD = 7cm
16. BC = 7cm, AD = 7cm
17. BC = $3\frac{1}{3}$cm, AD = $\frac{3}{5}$cm
18. BC = $3\frac{1}{3}$cm, AD = $2\frac{2}{5}$cm
19. BC = $5\frac{1}{3}$cm, AD = $2\frac{1}{4}$cm
20. BC = $3\frac{3}{4}$cm, AD = $2\frac{2}{3}$cm
21. BC = $2\frac{5}{8}$cm, AD = $1\frac{1}{3}$cm
22. BC = $6\frac{2}{3}$cm, AD = $4\frac{1}{2}$cm
23. BC = $2\frac{4}{5}$cm, AD = $2\frac{1}{7}$cm
24. BC = $3\frac{3}{8}$cm, AD = $2\frac{2}{3}$cm

Exercise 38

Find the area of triangle PRS when:

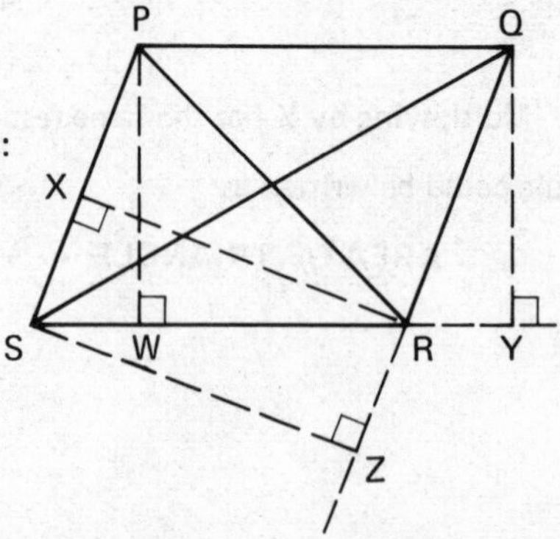

1. RS = 4cm, PW = 1·5cm
2. SR = 2·4cm, WP = 3cm
3. PS = 3·6cm, XR = 4cm
4. SP = 2·8cm, RX = 5cm

5. RS = 0·8cm, WP = 3cm
6. PS = 2·2cm, RX = 2·5cm
7. SR = 1·2cm, PW = 2·6cm
8. SP = 3·3cm, XR = 1·4cm
9. WP = 3·8cm, RS = 2·4cm
10. XR = 4·2cm, PS = 1·8cm

Find the area of triangle QRS when:

11. SR = 4cm, QY = 3cm
12. RS = 5cm, YQ = 6cm
13. SR = 5cm YQ = 5cm
14. RS = 3cm, QY = 7cm
15. RQ = 6cm, SZ = 3cm
16. RQ = 5cm, ZS = 4cm
17. QR = 3cm, SZ = 3cm
18. QR = 7cm, ZS = 7cm
19. SR = 0·6cm, PW = 2·5cm
20. RS = 1·4cm, WP = 3·5cm
21. QY = 1·2cm, PQ = 2·3cm
22. WP = 0·8cm, QP = 3·2cm
23. QR = 2·6cm, RX = 1·5cm
24. XR = 1·8cm, RQ = 2·3cm
25. PS = 2·4cm, SZ = 3·3cm
26. SP = 4·5cm, ZS = 1·8cm
27. SZ = 1·5cm, SP = 2·5cm
28. RS = 2·3cm, WP = 3·5cm
29. PQ = 3·4cm, YQ = 4·8cm
30. PS = 2·9cm, ZS = 3·6cm
31. If the area of PQRS = 42 cm^2 and QY = 6cm, find PQ.
32. If the area of PQYW = $56cm^2$ and PW = 7cm, find PQ.
33. If the area of XRZS = $96cm^2$ and SZ = 16cm, find XS.
34. If the area of RZSX = $384cm^2$ and RZ = 16cm, find XR.
35. If the area of ΔPRS = $8cm^2$ and SR = 4cm, find PW.
36. If the area of ΔPRS = $36cm^2$ and RX = 6cm, find PS.
37. If the area of ΔSRQ = $28cm^2$ and QY = 8cm, find SR.
38. If the area of ΔSRQ = $32cm^2$ and RQ = 8cm, find ZS.
39. If the area of ΔPRS = $25cm^2$ and RS = 5cm, find WP.
40. If the area of ΔSRQ = $35cm^2$ and SZ = 5cm, find QR.

8 Algebra

Exercise 39

Solve the following equations:

1.	$3x = 6$	**2.**	$4x = 16$	**3.**	$2x = 10$	**4.**	$2x = 8$
5.	$5x = 15$	**6.**	$3x = 18$	**7.**	$4x = 20$	**8.**	$6x = 6$
9.	$3x = 0$	**10.**	$14x = 70$	**11.**	$7x = 21$	**12.**	$9x = 81$

13. $2x - x = 3$

14. $4x = 11 - 3$

15. $5x - 2x = 12$

16. $6x = 22 - 4$

17. $3x + 2x = 25$

18. $5x = 13 + 2$

19. $x + 5x = 36$

20. $8x = 26 + 6$

21. $2x + 4x = 18 + 6$

22. $2x + 3x = 8 + 7$

23. $x + 5x + 7x = 20 + 8 + 11$

24. $2x + 3x + 4x = 7 + 9 + 11$

25. $2x + 3x - 4x = 18 - 9$

26. $3x + 4x - 5x = 8 + 6$

27. $9x - 5x = 16 + 4 - 8$

28. $7x + 3x = 24 + 6 - 20$

29. $7x - 9x + 15x = 17 + 9$

30. $x - 2x + 3x = 4 - 8 + 6$

More about simple equations

In the equations in Exercise 39 and previous work it was necessary to *'collect like terms'* on each side of the equation and then work out the value of x.

Let us look at question 29:

$$\begin{aligned} 7x - 9x + 15x &= 17 + 9 \\ 22x - 9x &= 26 \\ 13x &= 26 \\ x &= \frac{26}{13} \\ \text{Ans } x &= \underline{2} \end{aligned}$$

Now consider the following equations:

1. $3x + 2 = 17$
2. $9x = 24 - 3x$
3. $2x - 3 + 5 = 7 - 4x + x$
4. $5x - 7 = 8 + 3x$

To do these examples it is necessary to rearrange the positions of some terms in order to collect together the **unknowns on one side** of the equation and the **numbers on the other.**

Moving terms from one side to the other is called **transposing** terms, and it is common practice to arrange the unknowns on the left of the equation. We shall refer to the 'left-hand side' of the equation as LHS and to the 'right-hand side' as RHS.

We must now take care to keep the equation 'balanced', anything we do to the LHS we must also do to the RHS.

In Example 1 we have on the LHS a +2 which we do not want, we can get rid of it by **subtracting 2**, but the equation will now be unbalanced. To keep the balance we must subtract 2 from the RHS also.

In Example 2 we have an unwanted **−3x** on the RHS; **we can get rid of a minus quantity by adding.** We therefore add 3x **to both sides** of the equation.

REMEMBER

1 To get rid of a plus quantity (+) we subtract the quantity from both sides.
2 To get rid of a minus quantity (−) we add the quantity to both sides.

EXAMPLE 1

$$3x + 2 = 17$$

Subtract 2 from both sides: $3x = 17 - 2$
Collect like terms: $3x = 15$
Divide both sides by 3: $x = \frac{15}{3}$

Ans $\underline{x = 5}$

EXAMPLE 2

$$9x = 24 - 3x$$

Add 3x to both sides: $9x + 3x = 24$
Collect like terms: $12x = 24$
Divide both sides by 12: $x = \frac{24}{12}$

Ans $\underline{x = 2}$

EXAMPLE 3 $2x - 3 + 5 = 7 - 4x + x$

Collect like terms:	$2x + 2$	$= 7 - 3x$
Subtract 2 from both sides:	$2x$	$= 7 - 2 - 3x$
Add 3x to both sides:	$2x + 3x$	$= 7 - 2$
Collect like terms:	$5x$	$= 5$
Divide both sides by 5:	x	$= \frac{5}{5}$
Ans	x	$= 1$

EXAMPLE 4 $5x - 7 = 8 + 3x$

Add 7 to both sides:	$5x$	$= 8 + 7 + 3x$
Subtract 3x from both sides:	$5x - 3x$	$= 8 + 7$
Collect like terms:	$2x$	$= 15$
Divide both sides by 2:	x	$= \frac{15}{2}$
Ans	x	$= 7\frac{1}{2}$

Exercise 40

Solve the following equations:

1. $3x + 2 = 14$ **2.** $5x + 6 = 16$
3. $2x + 3 = 7$ **4.** $4x + 4 = 16$
5. $3x + 4 = 13$ **6.** $2x + 5 = 11$
7. $8x + 6 = 22$ **8.** $7x + 3 = 17$
9. $6x + 7 = 19$ **10.** $9x + 11 = 38$
11. $7x - 2 = 5$ **12.** $3x - 5 = 10$
13. $5x - 6 = 4$ **14.** $9x - 1 = 8$
15. $4x - 4 = 4$ **16.** $11x - 18 = 4$
17. $2x - 5 = 9$ **18.** $6x - 3 = 15$
19. $8x - 4 = 20$ **20.** $12x - 7 = 29$
21. $2x = 5 - 3x$ **22.** $3x = 8 - x$
23. $3x = 5 - 2x$ **24.** $9x = 20 - x$
25. $8x = 27 - x$ **26.** $13x = 22 - 9x$
27. $7x = 36 - 2x$ **28.** $6x = 50 - 4x$
29. $3x = 35 - 2x$ **30.** $5x = 48 - 7x$
31. $3x = 2x + 6$ **32.** $4x = 3x + 5$
33. $5x = 3x + 8$ **34.** $6x = 3x + 12$
35. $5x = 2x + 18$ **36.** $6x = 4x + 14$
37. $7x = 4x + 15$ **38.** $7x = 3x + 16$
39. $12x = 5x + 21$ **40.** $15x = 6x + 81$
41. $x - 3 = 3 - x$ **42.** $x + 3 = 3 - x$
43. $2x - 2 = 4 + x$ **44.** $5x + 6 = 3x + 12$

45. $3x - 7 = 7 - 4x$

46. $7x + 4 = 3x + 16$

47. $4x - 3 = 3x + 1$

48. $3x - 7 = 2x - 6$

49. $5x - 10 = 8 - 4x$

50. $12 - 6x = 18 - 12x$

51. $2x - 3 + 4 - 5x + 7 = 8 - 4x + 2 - 3x$

52. $5x + 6 - 7x + 2 - 3x = 7x + 16 - 11x - 14$

53. $9 - 4x + 3x - 7 - x = 13 - 9x + 4 + 2x$

54. $14x - 16 + 31 - 16x = 27x - 14 - 16x + 21 - x$

55. $21x + 17 - 13x - 29 = 23 - 9x + 16x - 35$

56. $6x - 4 + 3 - 8x + 5 = 3x + 7 + 4 - 7x$

57. $12 - 5x - 10 + 7x + 5 = 15 - 3x + 6 - 9x$

58. $2 + 3x - 16 - 9x + 5 = 2x + 7 + 12 - 12x - 6$

59. $x + 9 + 2x - 3 + 6x = 3 + 3x + 16 + 4x - 3$

60. $16x + 17 + 45x = 18 + 32x + 28$

Directed numbers

We can sometimes obtain answers which are **minus quantities**, for example, **−5, −4x, −2½.** This type of answer is easier to understand if we consider the Centigrade (Celsius) thermometer. The temperature readings are always given with reference to 0° (the freezing point of water).

Thus:	60°C	means 60° above	0°C
	92°C	means 92° above	0°C
	31°C	means 31° above	0°C
But	−2°C	means 2° below	0°C
	−8°C	means 8° below	0°C
	−35°C	means 35° below	0°C

You will see that it is necessary to draw **special attention** to those readings **less than 0°C**, and we do so by using the **minus sign**.

The sign is not used in the sense of 'subtracting' or 'taking away', instead it indicates the **direction** of a reading with reference to zero (0°C).

−35°C is called a **negative** quantity

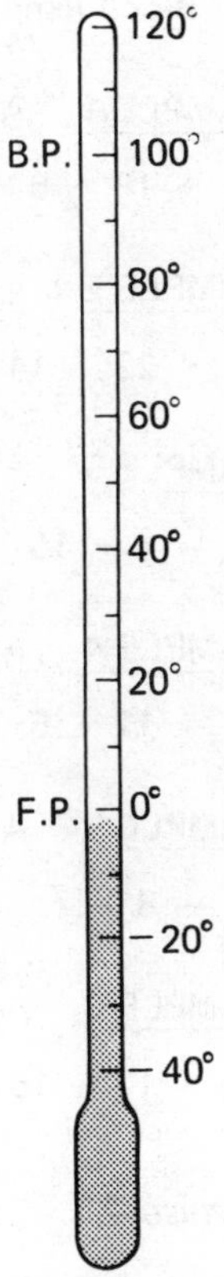

centigrade thermometer

Those readings *above* zero are regarded as *normal* and no special attention is given to the sign, but in fact 92°C could be written as + 92°C. It can be called a **positive** quantity and the quantities used in everyday life are of this type. For example, a second-hand car may be advertised at £500 NOT +£500.

QUESTIONS

1 If FP stands for the Freezing Point of water (0°C), what does BP (100°C) stand for?
2 What would be your reaction to an advertisement in which the price of a car was given as −£500?
3 Is zero (0) a positive or a negative quantity?

SOME TEMPERATURES TO REMEMBER

Freezing point	=	0°C	Cold weather	=	5°C
Warm room	=	20°C	Hot weather	=	30°C
Blood temp.	=	36·8°C	Boiling point	=	100°C

EXAMPLE 1 A thermometer reads 18°C, the temperature rises 6°C

$+18+6=+24=\underline{24°C}$

EXAMPLE 2 A thermometer reads 22°C, the temperature falls 14°C.

$+22-14=+8=\underline{8°C}$

EXAMPLE 3 A thermometer reads −5°C, the temperature rises 10°C.

$-5+10=+5=\underline{5°C}$

EXAMPLE 4 A thermometer reads −12°C, the temperature rises 5°C.

$-12+5=-7=\underline{-7°C}$

EXAMPLE 5 A thermometer reads −8°C, the temperature falls 7°C.

$-8-7=-15=\underline{-15°C}$

EXAMPLE 6 A thermometer reads 12°C, the temperature falls 16°C.

$+12-16=-4=\underline{-4°C}$

Exercise 41

Write the following statements using **directed** numbers. Give the final result.

1 A thermometer reads 13°C, the temperature rises 3°C.
2 A thermometer reads 15°C, the temperature rises 4°C.
3 A thermometer reads 17°C, the temperature rises 6°C.
4 A thermometer reads 23°C, the temperature falls 5°C.

5 A thermometer reads 27° C, the temperature falls 9° C.
6 A thermometer reads 32° C, the temperature falls 13° C.
7 A thermometer reads 0° C, the temperature rises 4° C.
8 A thermometer reads −2 °C, the temperature rises 7° C.
9 A thermometer reads −5° C, the temperature rises 11° C.
10 A thermometer reads 6° C, the temperature falls 8° C.
11 A thermometer reads 9° C, the temperature falls 10° C.
12 A thermometer reads 14 °C, the temperature falls 20° C.
13 A thermometer reads 0 °C, the temperature falls 3° C.
14 A thermometer reads −3 °C, the temperature falls 5° C.
15 A thermometer reads −8 °C, the temperature falls 7° C.
16 A thermometer reads −4 °C, the temperature rises 2° C.
17 A thermometer reads −7° C, the temperature rises 4° C.
18 A thermometer reads −11 °C, the temperature rises 9° C.
19 At midday a thermometer reads 20° C, at midnight it has fallen by 8° C, by 3 a.m. it has fallen a further 3° C.
20 At midday a thermometer reads 28° C, at midnight it has fallen by 12° C, by 4 a.m. it has fallen a further 4° C.
21 At midday a thermometer reads 35° C, at midnight it has fallen by 15° C, by 2 a.m. it has fallen a further 8° C.
22 At midnight a thermometer reads 0° C, at 4 a.m. it has risen by 3° C, by 8 a.m. it has risen a further 3° C.
23 At midnight a thermometer reads −5° C, at 6 a.m. it has risen by 4° C, by midday it has risen a further 8° C.
24 At midnight a thermometer reads −4° C, at 3 a.m. it has fallen by 5° C, by midday it has risen by 12° C.
25 A thermometer reads − 6° C, a later reading gives 7° C. What is the change in temperature?
26 A thermometer reads −11° C, a later reading gives 3° C. What is the change in temperature?
27 A thermometer reads −14° C, a later reading gives −3° C. What is the change in temperature?
28 A thermometer reads 12° C, a later reading gives 2° C. What is the change in temperature?
29 A thermometer reads 8° C, a later reading gives −4° C. What is the change in termperature?
30 A thermometer reads −2° C, a later reading gives −7° C. What is the change in temperature?

Directed numbers: addition and subtraction

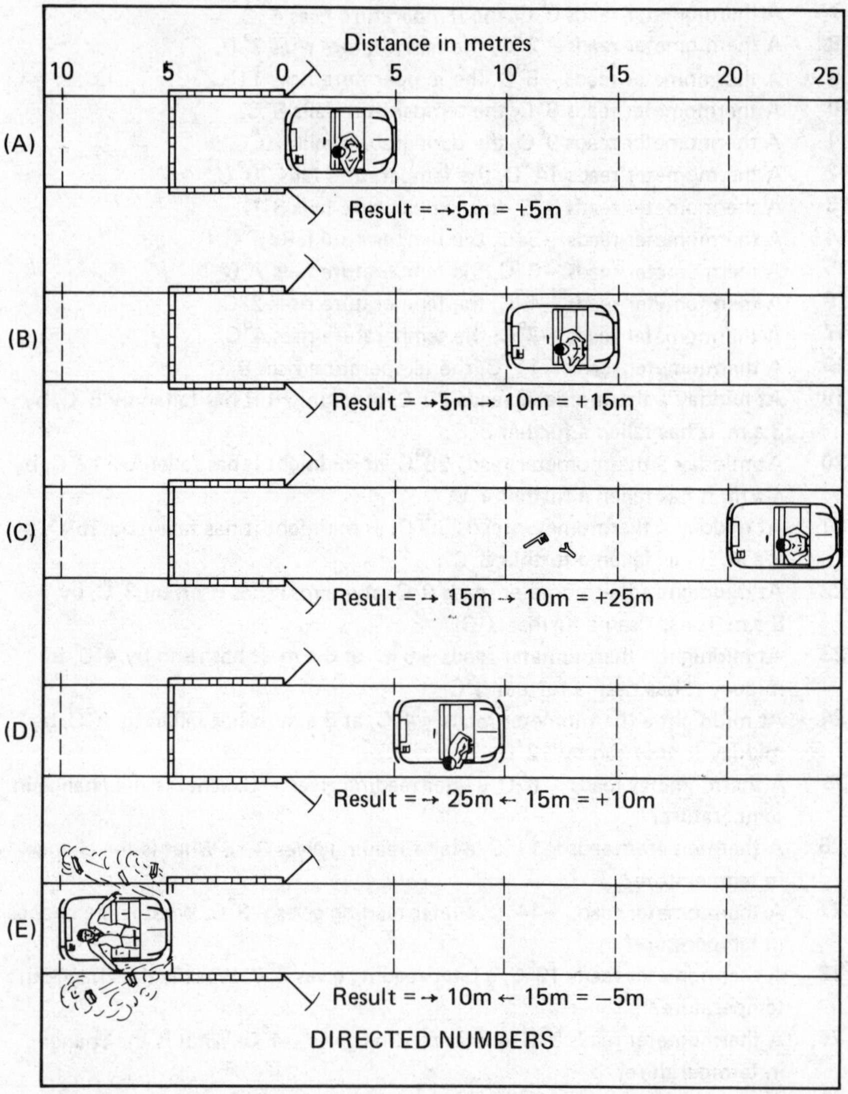

We now have to learn to use positive and negative (directed) numbers in operations such as addition and subtraction. The diagram above gives a further illustration of directed numbers; it shows the movements of a car on a narrow drive. The garage doors are the reference line or zero (0 metres) and distances are measured to the front bumper.

1 From A you will see the car has moved **forward** 5m

Thus: $\rightarrow$ 5m = + 5m

2 From B you will see that the car has moved **forward** a further 10m. That is a gain of 10m on the previous position.

Thus: $\rightarrow$ 5m $\rightarrow$ 10m = + 5m + 10m = + 15m

3 In C the car has moved **forward** a further 10m from the previous position.

Thus: $\rightarrow$ 15m $\rightarrow$ 10m = + 15m + 10m = + 25m

4 From C we can see the owner has left some tools behind and must therefore **reverse** to the position shown in D.

Thus: $\rightarrow$ 25m $\leftarrow$ 15m = + 25m − 15m = + 10m

5 From E we can see the result of bad driving and from the previous position the situation now is

Thus: $\rightarrow$ 10m $\leftarrow$ 15m = + 10m − 15m = −5m

We can summarize these results as follows:

+ means $\rightarrow$ the NORMAL procedure,
− means $\leftarrow$ the REVERSE (or opposite) to normal procedure.

With these results in mind, let us give meaning to the following:

EXAMPLE 1 4 + (+ 2)

(a) Having no sign attached to it, the number 4 is a normal positive value.
(b) Next we have to add (+ 2), but the + sign can be read as 'do the normal thing to that which follows'; thus 'do the normal thing' with (+ 2) is to 'add 2' to 4.
$\therefore$ **4 + (+ 2) means 4 + 2 = 6**

EXAMPLE 2 5 + (−3)

(a) Having no sign attached to it, the number 5 is a normal positive value.
(b) Next we have to add (−3), but the + sign can be read as 'do the normal thing to that which follows'; thus 'do the normal thing' with (−3) is to 'subtract 3' from 5.
$\therefore$ **5 + (− 3) means 5 − 3 = 2**

EXAMPLE 3 6 − (+ 4)

(a) Having no sign attached to it, the number 6 is a normal positive value.

(b) Next we have to subtract (+ 4), but the − sign can be read as 'do the opposite thing to that which follows'; thus 'do the opposite thing' with (+ 4) is to 'subtract 4' from 6.

∴ 6 − (+ 4) means 6 − 4 = 2

EXAMPLE 4   7 − (− 5)

(a) The number 7 is a normal positive value.

(b) − (− 5) means 'do the opposite thing with (− 5)

∴ 7 − (−5) means 7 + 5 = 12

The complete set of sign values is as follows:

+ (+) means +
− (−) means +   } like signs give '*plus*'

+ (−) means −
− (+) means −   } unlike signs give '*minus*'

This is known as **The Rule of Signs.**

Exercise 42

Write down the values of the following:

1. + (+ 2)	**2.** + (+ 4)	**3.** + (+ 5)
4. + (+ 1)	**5.** + (+ 7)	**6.** + (+ 3)
7. + (+ 8)	**8.** + (+ 10)	**9.** + (+ 12)
10. + (+ 9)	**11.** + (+ 0)	**12.** + (+ 6)
13. + (− 1)	**14.** + (−5)	**15.** + (−3)
16. + (−2)	**17.** + (−7)	**18.** + (−4)
19. + (−6)	**20.** + (−10)	**21.** + (−8)
22. + (−9)	**23.** + (−20)	**24.** + (−16)
25. −(+ 3)	**26.** −(+ 1)	**27.** −(+ 5)
28. −(+ 4)	**29.** −(+ 6)	**30.** −(+ 2)
31. −(+ 9)	**32.** −(+ 7)	**33.** −(+ 10)
34. −(+ 8)	**35.** −(+ 11)	**36.** −(+ 18)
37. −(−2)	**38.** −(−4)	**39.** −(−1)
40. −(−6)	**41.** −(−3)	**42.** −(−9)
43. −(−5)	**44.** −(−8)	**45.** −(−10)
46. −(−7)	**47.** −(−15)	**48.** −(−30)
49. 8 + (−3)	**50.** 3 − (−8)	**51.** 8 − (−3)
52. 7 − (+ 4)	**53.** 4 − (−7)	**54.** 7 + (−4)
55. 9 + (−5)	**56.** 9 − (+ 5)	**57.** 5 − (−9)
58. 0 + (+ 2)	**59.** 2 − (+ 0)	**60.** 6 + (−4)

61.	2 – (+ 2)	**62.**	2 + (–2)	**63.**	2 – (–2)
64.	(– 1) + (– 1)	**65.**	(–2) + (+ 2)	**66.**	(–3) – (–3)
67.	(+ 4) – (+ 4)	**68.**	(–6) + (–2)	**69.**	(–2) + (–6)
70.	(– 1) – (–0)	**71.**	(–0) + (– 1)	**72.**	(– 1) – (– 1)
73.	(–7) + (+ 7)	**74.**	(–2) + (+ 4)	**75.**	(+ 5) – (+ 3)
76.	(+ x) + (+ x)	**77.**	(+ x) – (+ x)	**78.**	(–x) + (–x)
79.	(–2x) – (–3x)	**80.**	(+ 3x) + (–2x)	**81.**	(+ 2x) – (+ 3x)
82.	(–6y) + (+ 8y)	**83.**	(+ 4a) + (–4a)	**84.**	(0) – (–3b)
85.	(+ 3x) + (–0)	**86.**	9x + (–3x)	**87.**	(3x) – (+ 9x)
88.	(–3x) – (–3x)	**89.**	(4x) – (+ 2x)	**90.**	(2x) – (–4x)
91.	(–4x) – (–3x)	**92.**	(–5x) + (+ 3x)	**93.**	(6x) – (+ 8x)
94.	(–7x) – (–5x)	**95.**	(–9x) + (+ 3x)	**96.**	(3x) – (–9x)
97.	(–6x) + (–3x)	**98.**	(–3x) – (+ 6x)	**99.**	(–3x) – (–6x)

9 More about decimal and vulgar fractions

Approximations

Whenever we try to make **practical** measurements we most often find that it is impossible to give an **exact and precise** value for a result. The accuracy of any measurement will depend on the quality of the measuring equipment and the care and patience of the person using it.

Consider the difficulty of making accurate measurements in the following examples:

<u>LENGTH</u> A shopkeeper may have to measure material which tends to stretch – elastic for PE shorts would be a good example.

<u>WEIGHT</u> The greengrocer finds it very difficult to weigh **exactly** 2 lb (or 1 kg) of tomatoes.

<u>VOLUME</u> The petrol-pump attendant must rely on the accuracy of dials on the pump when supplying 2 gal (or 9 l) of petrol. Remember there will be small traces of petrol left in the pipe.

<u>TIME</u> The PE staff at your school would have much trouble in *timing* a 100m sprint event using an ordinary wrist or pocket watch.

There are laws to protect the consumer (customer) against tradesmen who give **short-measure** (*Weights and Measurements Acts*), and, to protect themselves, shopkeepers often give a little more than the quantity asked for. The draper will certainly not stretch the material and will give a centimetre or so extra. The greengrocer will tell the housewife that he has weighed a 'little more' or a 'little less' than the 2 lb (or 1 kg) of tomatoes and he will tell her the cost from a price-scale on his weighing machine. The accuracy of *timing* races depends on using *stop-watches* which are generally accurate to 1/10 second (0·1 sec), though for very important occasions the timing equipment is accurate to 1/100 second (0·01 sec).

These examples show that the results obtained when measuring are given as **close approximations** since we cannot state an **exact** value for the answer.

We sometimes have to carry out an approximation in our calculations:

EXAMPLE   40 ÷ 6

```
        6·666-----
     ___________________
   6 )40·000 000 000
      36 ↓ |
      ___  |
       4 0 |
       3 6 ↓
      _____
         40
         36 ↓
        ____
          40
          36
          __
           ----
```

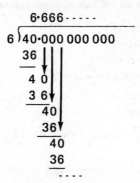

It seems fairly certain that this calculation could go on forever because we can keep on 'bringing down noughts' and every time we divide by 6 it goes '6 times' (in the answer line). When we 'take away' we are left with 4 every time and so it goes on and on.

To deal with such a situation, we have to give an approximate answer and to show how accurate the answer is we tell people the number of decimal places we have used.

Correct to a given decimal place

To give an answer correct to a given number of decimal places, we work to **one more place** than we are asked for. We then consider the **value of this extra figure**, if less than **5** we ignore it; if **5 or more, the figure in front of it is increased by one.**

EXAMPLE   Consider the number 25·6375

NOTE
1   The 25 is a whole number.
2   The digits 6 3 7 5 occupy the first, second, third and fourth decimal places.

Now to consider the number 26·6375

A   25·6 = 26 (correct to the nearest whole number)

B   25·63 = 25·6 (correct to 1 decimal place)

C   25·637 = 25·64 (correct to 2 decimal places)

D   25·6375 = 25·638 (correct to 3 decimal places)

NOTE

1. 3·5 suggests a number correct to one decimal place.
2. 3·50 suggests a number correct to two decimal places.
3. The answer to the question 40 ÷ 6 can be given several ways:

6·667	(correct to 3 dec. pl.)
6·67	(correct to 2 dec. pl.)
6·7	(correct to 1 dec. pl.)
7	(correct to nearest whole number)

Exercise 43

Express the following correct to the nearest whole number:

1. 6·1	**2.** 5·4	**3.** 7·2	**4.** 8·3
5. 2·7	**6.** 1·9	**7.** 3·6	**8.** 4·8
9. 8·5	**10.** 9·2	**11.** 5·8	**12.** 2·1
13. 12·4	**14.** 16·8	**15.** 18·3	**16.** 14·6
17. 21·5	**18.** 25·2	**19.** 26·7	**20.** 27·3
21. 32·8	**22.** 34·1	**23.** 37·4	**24.** 38·6
25. 40·2	**26.** 40·4	**27.** 40·6	**28.** 40·9
29. 49·3	**30.** 49·7	**31.** 49·1	**32.** 49·8
33. 50·5	**34.** 59·4	**35.** 69·9	**36.** 70·1
37. 124·2	**38.** 235·6	**39.** 359·7	**40.** 406·4

Exercise 44

Express the following correct to one decimal place: (REMEMBER You look at the figure in the *second decimal place*)

1. 2·52	**2.** 4·43	**3.** 5·31	**4.** 3·24
5. 1·36	**6.** 6·29	**7.** 8·47	**8.** 7·68
9. 9·42	**10.** 1·35	**11.** 5·59	**12.** 6·21
13. 0·15	**14.** 0·73	**15.** 0·96	**16.** 0·92
17. 10·98	**18.** 10·06	**19.** 10·82	**20.** 10·87
21. 12·153	**22.** 14·224	**23.** 16·342	**24.** 18·521
25. 20·982	**26.** 25·973	**27.** 27·964	**28.** 29·951
29. 31·326	**30.** 33·437	**31.** 45·149	**32.** 56·218
33. 62·452	**34.** 71·536	**35.** 82·764	**36.** 99·983
37. 106·24	**38.** 110·45	**39.** 100·04	**40.** 999·96

Exercise 45

Express the following correct to (A) two dec. pl., (B) three dec. pl.:

1. 0·1234	**2.** 1·3454	**3.** 23·4565	**4.** 12·5673
5. 5·0505	**6.** 7·1053	**7.** 9·5151	**8.** 6·7545
9. 0·9009	**10.** 2·3345	**11.** 4·0636	**12.** 3·1549

13.	5·2753	**14.**	0·5555	**15.**	8·3333	**16.**	7·4556
17.	1·0006	**18.**	3·1001	**19.**	2·1027	**20.**	0·0001

Exercise 46

Find the value of the following, giving your answers correct to one decimal place:

1.	3·7 × 2·3	**2.**	5·1 × 3·4	**3.**	7·3 × 4·6	**4.**	509 ÷ 14
5.	60·7 ÷ 1·7	**6.**	7·23 ÷ 0·23	**7.**	9·5 × 6·7	**8.**	1·01 × 3·3
9.	12·4 × 5·9	**10.**	74·9 ÷ 2·7	**11.**	825 ÷ 32	**12.**	0·863 ÷ 0·048
13.	2·31 × 9·3	**14.**	0·464 × 10·7	**15.**	94·7 ÷ 5·6		

Exercise 47

Express the following sums of money in £s, correct to (A) the nearest penny, (B) the nearest £:

1.	£7.054	**2.**	£2.715	**3.**	£3.508	**4.**	£6.494
5.	82·7p	**6.**	123·3p	**7.**	9·61p	**8.**	10·87p
9.	£4.626	**10.**	£4.602	**11.**	£4.006	**12.**	£4.206
13.	200·7p	**14.**	207·7p	**15.**	270·7p	**16.**	277·2p
17.	£8.154	**18.**	£80.541	**19.**	£80.045	**20.**	£80.005

Changing decimals to vulgar fractions

From our earlier work, we should know that:

$$0{\cdot}1 = \frac{1}{10}, \qquad 0{\cdot}01 = \frac{1}{100}, \qquad 0{\cdot}001 = \frac{1}{1000}$$

It should be clear that:

$$0{\cdot}6 = \frac{6}{10}, \qquad 0{\cdot}07 = \frac{7}{100}, \qquad 0{\cdot}005 = \frac{5}{1000}$$

If the decimals are added, we get **0·675**.

$$\text{Then } 0{\cdot}675 = \frac{6}{10} + \frac{7}{100} + \frac{5}{1000}$$

$$= \frac{600 + 70 + 5}{100} = \frac{675}{1000}$$

$$\therefore \quad 0{\cdot}675 = \frac{\cancel{675}^{135}}{\cancel{1000}_{200}} = \frac{\cancel{135}^{27}}{\cancel{200}_{40}} = \underline{\frac{27}{40}}$$

The result $\mathbf{0{\cdot}675 = \frac{675}{1000}}$ shows that we can easily make up a **rule for changing decimal fractions to vulgar fractions:**

RULE

The number on top (numerator) is formed by using the digits (figures) in the decimal; the number underneath (denominator) is formed by placing a figure 1 for the decimal point and a nought for each digit after it.

NOTE The resulting vulgar fraction may not be in its lowest terms, and 'cancelling' may be necessary – for example

$$0{\cdot}675 = \frac{675}{1000} = \frac{27}{40}$$

Exercise 48

Change the following decimals to vulgar fractions, giving the answers in their lowest terms:

1.	0·5	**2.**	0·25	**3.**	0·75	**4.**	0·125	**5.**	0·375
6.	0·625	**7.**	0·875	**8.**	0·2	**9.**	0·4	**10.**	0·6
11.	0·8	**12.**	0·3	**13.**	0·1	**14.**	0·7	**15.**	0·9
16.	0·24	**17.**	0·36	**18.**	0·48	**19.**	0·72	**20.**	0·84
21.	0·96	**22.**	0·15	**23.**	0·45	**24.**	0·12	**25.**	0·05
26.	0·025	**27.**	0·015	**28.**	0·55	**29.**	0·08	**30.**	0·105
31.	0·95	**32.**	0·104	**33.**	0·18	**34.**	0·005	**35.**	0·395
36.	0·425	**37.**	0·205	**38.**	0·416	**39.**	0·725	**40.**	0·123

Changing vulgar fractions to decimals

To change a vulgar fraction to a decimal we divide the number underneath into the number on top.

RULE **Divide the denominator into the numerator**

EXAMPLE Express $\frac{7}{8}$ as a decimal

```
     0·8 7 5
   ---------
 8 ) 7·0 0 0
     6 4
     ---
       6 0
       5 6
       ---
         4 0
         4 0
         ===
```

Ans = 0·875

NOTE

1 The result we have just obtained, together with numbers 1-11 of Exercise 48, should be 'learnt by heart'.
2 Some decimal values may have to be given as approximations (correct to a number of decimal places).
3 Some fractions give a recurring figure in the decimal; this may be indicated by a dot placed above the recurring figure. Thus

$$\frac{1}{3} = 0{\cdot}33\dot{3}$$

This method is rarely used, however; instead an approximation (corrected value) is usually given:

$$\frac{1}{3} = 0{\cdot}333 \text{ (corr. to 3 dec. pl.)}$$

Exercise 49

Change the following vulgar fractions to decimals, giving the answers correct to three decimal places where necessary:

1. $\frac{1}{2}$	**2.** $\frac{1}{4}$	**3.** $\frac{3}{4}$	**4.** $\frac{1}{8}$	**5.** $\frac{3}{8}$
6. $\frac{5}{8}$	**7.** $\frac{7}{8}$	**8.** $\frac{1}{5}$	**9.** $\frac{2}{5}$	**10.** $\frac{3}{5}$
11. $\frac{4}{5}$	**12.** $\frac{3}{10}$	**13.** $\frac{7}{10}$	**14.** $\frac{9}{10}$	**15.** $\frac{1}{3}$
16. $\frac{2}{3}$	**17.** $\frac{1}{6}$	**18.** $\frac{5}{6}$	**19.** $\frac{3}{20}$	**20.** $\frac{7}{20}$
21. $\frac{9}{20}$	**22.** $\frac{11}{20}$	**23.** $\frac{13}{20}$	**24.** $\frac{17}{20}$	**25.** $\frac{19}{20}$
26. $\frac{1}{16}$	**27.** $\frac{3}{16}$	**28.** $\frac{5}{16}$	**29.** $\frac{7}{16}$	**30.** $\frac{9}{16}$
31. $\frac{11}{16}$	**32.** $\frac{13}{16}$	**33.** $\frac{15}{16}$	**34.** $\frac{2}{15}$	**35.** $\frac{7}{15}$
36. $\frac{4}{25}$	**37.** $\frac{18}{25}$	**38.** $\frac{27}{40}$	**39.** $\frac{22}{35}$	**40.** $\frac{19}{30}$

10 Percentage

A fraction such as ¾ may be written as $\frac{75}{100}$; in this form it represents 75 parts as a fraction of 100 parts and is called **75 per cent.**

The words *per cent* mean 'out of each hundred' and the abbreviation is **%**.

75% = 75 per cent

A percentage is a fraction whose denominator is 100.

NOTE Century, centurion, centigrade, centipede, centime are all words concerned with 100. What is the meaning of each?

RULES

1 Fractions or decimals to percentages

MULTIPLY BY $\frac{100}{1}$ (OR 100)

EXAMPLES

(a) $\frac{5}{8} = \left(\frac{5}{\cancel{8}_2} \times \frac{\cancel{100}^{25}}{1}\right)\% = \frac{125}{2}\% = \underline{62\frac{1}{2}\%}$

(b) $0{\cdot}375 = (0{\cdot}375 \times 100)\% = \underline{37{\cdot}5\%}$

In this way we take a fraction of 100 parts instead of 1 whole one.

2 Percentages to fractions or decimals

EXPRESS AS A FRACTION WHOSE DENOMINATOR IS 100

OR MULTIPLY BY $\frac{1}{100}$

EXAMPLES

(a) $60\% = \frac{\cancel{60}^3}{\cancel{100}_5} = \underline{\frac{3}{5}}$

(b) $43\% = \frac{43}{100} = \underline{0{\cdot}43}$

(c) $12\frac{1}{2}\% = \frac{12\frac{1}{2}}{100} = \frac{12{\cdot}5}{100} = \underline{0{\cdot}125}$

OR $= \left(12\frac{1}{2} \times \frac{1}{100}\right) = \frac{\cancel{25}^{1}}{2} \times \frac{1}{\cancel{100}_{4}} = \underline{\frac{1}{8}}$

Exercise 50

Express the following as percentages:

1. $\frac{1}{4}$	2. $\frac{1}{2}$	3. $\frac{3}{4}$	4. $\frac{1}{8}$	5. $\frac{3}{8}$
6. $\frac{5}{8}$	7. $\frac{1}{3}$	8. $\frac{2}{3}$	9. $\frac{1}{6}$	10. $\frac{5}{6}$
11. $\frac{7}{8}$	12. $\frac{1}{12}$	13. $\frac{5}{12}$	14. $\frac{1}{10}$	15. $\frac{3}{10}$
16. $\frac{7}{10}$	17. $\frac{1}{5}$	18. $\frac{2}{5}$	19. $\frac{3}{5}$	20. $\frac{4}{5}$
21. $\frac{1}{20}$	22. $\frac{3}{20}$	23. $\frac{7}{20}$	24. $\frac{9}{20}$	25. $\frac{11}{20}$
26. $\frac{13}{20}$	27. $\frac{17}{20}$	28. $\frac{19}{20}$	29. $\frac{1}{25}$	30. $\frac{4}{25}$
31. $\frac{9}{25}$	32. $\frac{17}{25}$	33. $\frac{21}{25}$	34. $\frac{23}{40}$	35. $\frac{37}{40}$
36. $\frac{17}{50}$	37. $\frac{29}{50}$	38. $\frac{43}{50}$	39. $\frac{37}{75}$	40. $\frac{123}{125}$
41. 0·5	42. 0·75	43. 0·25	44. $0{\cdot}3\dot{3}$	45. $0{\cdot}6\dot{6}$
46. 0·6	47. 0·8	48. 0·57	49. 0·85	50. 0·92
51. 0·125	52. 0·235	53. 0·324	54. 0·721	55. 0·826
56. 0·025	57. 0·05	58. 1·5	59. 1·05	60. 0·15

Exercise 51

Express the following (A) as fractions in their lowest terms, (B) as decimals:

1. 5%	2. 10%	3. 20%	4. 30%	5. 40%
6. 50%	7. 60%	8. 70%	9. 80%	10. 90%
11. 100%	12. 150%	13. 25%	14. 75%	15. 15%
16. 35%	17. 45%	18. 55%	19. 65%	20. 85%
21. 95%	22. 37½%	23. 62½%	24. 87½%	25. 2%

26.	6%	**27.**	8%	**28.**	4%	**29.**	$33\frac{1}{3}\%$	**30.**	$66\frac{2}{3}\%$
31.	7·5%	**32.**	2·5%	**33.**	3·75%	**34.**	6·25%	**35.**	8·75%
36.	32·5%	**37.**	42·5%	**38.**	52·5%	**39.**	72·5%	**40.**	82·5%

Quantities as percentages

EXAMPLE 1 Express £5.80 as a percentage of £25

First express £5.80 as a fraction of £25: $= \frac{£5.80}{£25}$

Now multiply the fraction by $\frac{100}{1}$ to obtain the percentage: $= \left(\frac{5{\cdot}8}{\cancel{25}_1} \times \frac{\cancel{100}^4}{1}\right)\%$ ★

Ans $=$ $\underline{23{\cdot}2\%}$

NOTE ★ The £ signs disappear at this stage.

EXAMPLE 2 Find 37½% of £24

First express 37½% as a fraction of 100: $= \frac{37\frac{1}{2}}{100}$ OR $\left(\frac{75}{2} \times \frac{1}{100}\right)$

Now multiply £24 by this fraction: $= \frac{£24}{1} \times \frac{\cancel{75}^3}{2} \times \frac{1}{\cancel{100}_4}$

$= \frac{£\cancel{24}^3}{1} \times \frac{3}{\cancel{8}_1}$

Ans $=$ $\underline{£9}$

Exercise 52

Express the first quantity as a percentage of the second quantity: (*give answers correct to 1 dec. pl. where necessary*)

1. £3 ; £5
2. £4 ; £5
3. £3 ; £10
4. £7 ; £10
5. £6 ; £12
6. £6 ; £18
7. £6 ; £24
8. £5 ; £20
9. £5 ; £25
10. £3.25 ; £5
11. £4.73 ; £10
12. £6.39 ; £15
13. 1·6g ; 4g
14. 2·7g ; 3g
15. 43km ; 50km
16. 0·385km ; 5km
17. 3·6 litres ; 24 litres
18. 6·3 litres ; 9 litres

19. 4·8g ; 24g

20. 5·6g ; 35g

21. 72m ; 125m

22. 8·1m ; 90 m

23. 6·4 litres ; 7·2 litres

24. 1·75 litres ; 5·25 litres

25. Find 10% of £1

26. Find 10% of £30

27. Find 20% of £1

28. Find 20% of £50

29. Find 20% of £75

30. Find 20% of £100

31. Find 25% of £1

32. Find 25% of £4

33. Find 25% of £20

34. Find 25% of £100

35. Find 50% of £1

36. Find 50% of £10

37. Find 50% of £25

38. Find 50% of £100

39. Find 50% of £200

40. Find 50% of £250

41. Find 75% of £1

42. Find 75% of £4

43. Find 75% of £20

44. Find 75% of £60

45. Find 75% of £100

46. Find 75% of £400

47. Find $33\frac{1}{3}$% of 90p

48. Find $33\frac{1}{3}$% of £9

49. Find $33\frac{1}{3}$% of £15

50. Find $33\frac{1}{3}$% of £75

51. Find $66\frac{2}{3}$% of £1.20

52. Find $66\frac{2}{3}$% of £24

53. Find $66\frac{2}{3}$% of £57

54. Find $66\frac{2}{3}$% of £150

55. Find 27% of £1

56. Find 39% of £1

57. Find 52% of £1

58. Find 67% of £1

59. Find 52% of £1.50

60. Find 68% of £2.25

61. Find, correct to the nearest penny, 70% of £16.07

62. Find, correct to the nearest penny, 60% of £2.82

63. Find, correct to the nearest penny, 17½% of £8.20

64. Find, correct to 2 dec. pl., 15% of 9·27m

65. Find, correct to the nearest kilometre, 28% of 82km.

66. Find, correct to 1 dec. pl., 57% of 12cm

67. Find, correct to 2 dec. pl., 35% of 1·25kg

68. Find, correct to 2 dec. pl., 38½% of 3·35kg

69. Find, correct to 1 dec. pl., 65% of 85 litres

70. Find, correct to 1 dec. pl., 36% of 24 litres.

11 Angles

Revision

A **The sum of the angles at a point is 360°**

$\angle a + \angle b + \angle c + \angle d + \angle e = 360°$

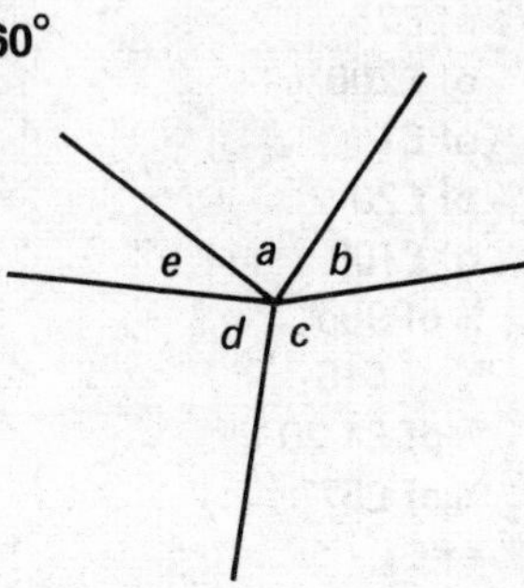

B **The sum of the angles on a straight line is 180°**

$\angle x + \angle y + \angle z = 180°$

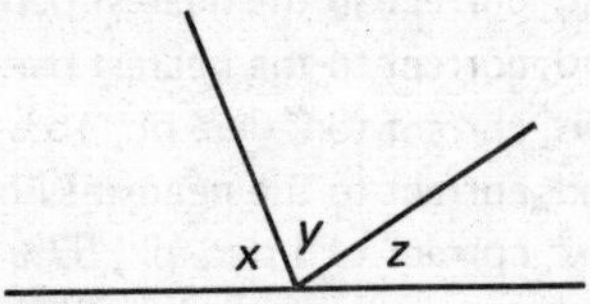

C **The sum of the exterior angles of any polygon is 360°**

$\angle a + \angle b + \angle c + \angle d + \angle e = 360°$

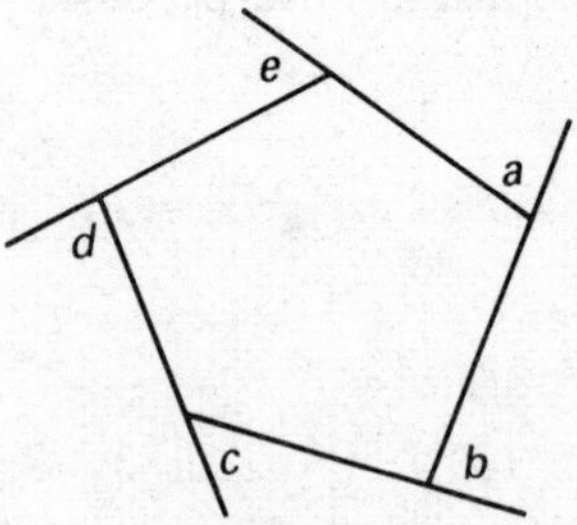

D **The sum of the interior angles of any polygon is:**

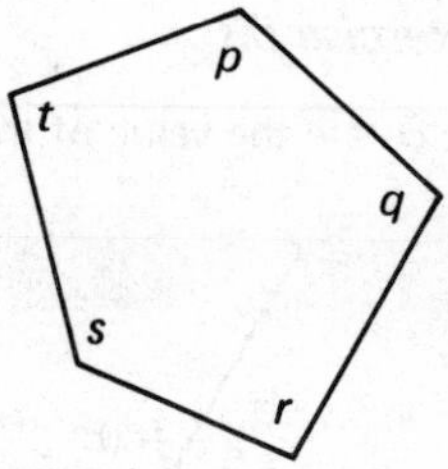

(2N – 4) right-angles

$\angle p + \angle q + \angle r + \angle s + \angle t = 6 \text{ rt} \angle s = 540^\circ$

NOTE

1 **N is the number of sides** in the polygon.
2 **A regular polygon** is one in which the **sides are** equal, the **interior angles are equal**, the **exterior angles are equal.**

E **The sum of the interior angles of a triangle is 180°**

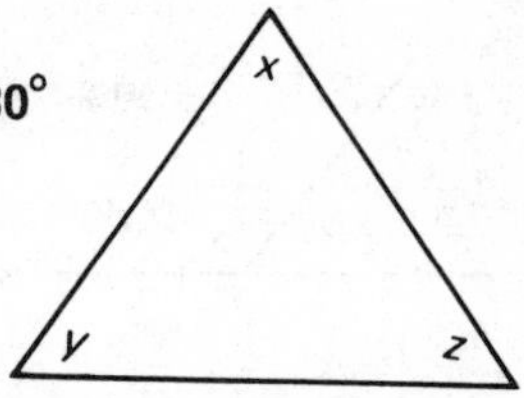

$\angle x + \angle y + \angle z = 180^\circ$

Check with formula

F **The sum of the interior angles of a quarilateral is 360°**

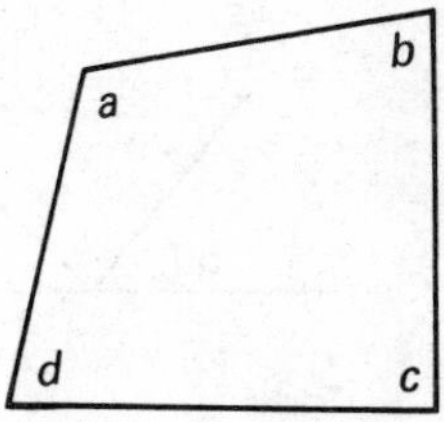

$\angle a + \angle b + \angle c + \angle d = 360^\circ$

Check with formula

G **The opposite angles of a parallelogram are equal**

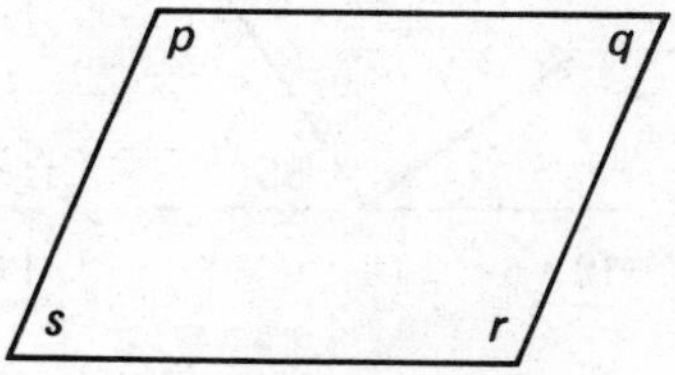

$\angle p + \angle q + \angle r + \angle s = 360^\circ$
$\angle p = \angle r$
$\angle q = \angle s$
$\angle p + \angle q = 180^\circ$
$\angle p + \angle s = 180^\circ$
$\angle q + \angle p = 180^\circ$
$\angle q + \angle r = 180^\circ$
$\angle r + \angle q = 180^\circ$
$\angle r + \angle s = 180^\circ$
$\angle s + \angle r = 180^\circ$
$\angle s + \angle p = 180^\circ$

NOTE In a parallelogram, angles which are next to each other (adjacent) add up to 180°.

Exercise 53

Calculate the value of the lettered angles in the following diagrams:

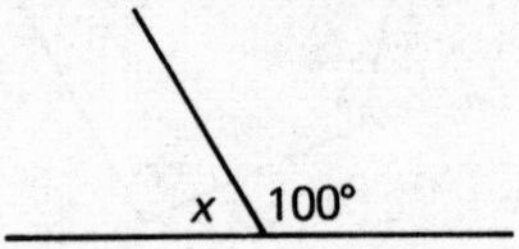

1

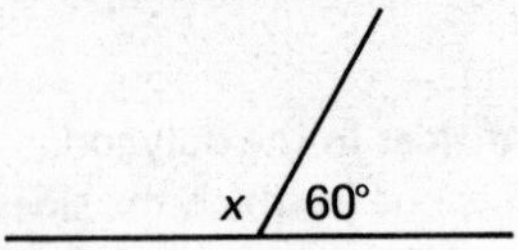

2

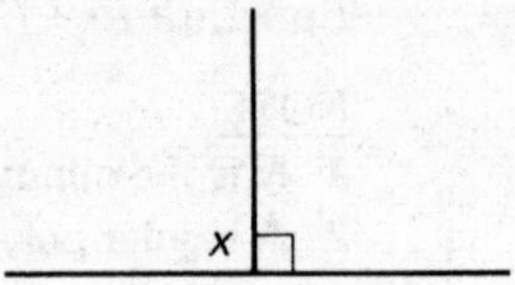

3

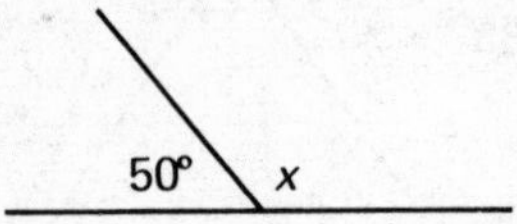

4

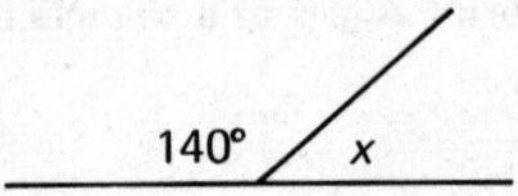

5

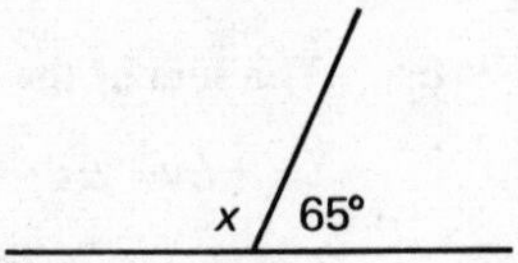

6

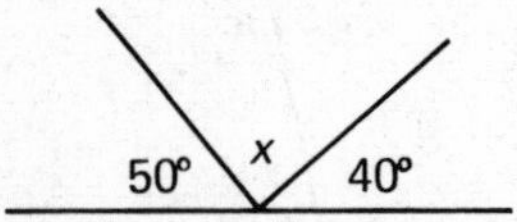

7

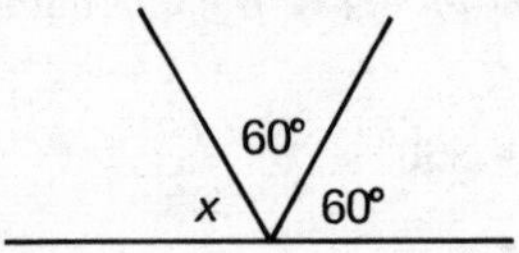

8

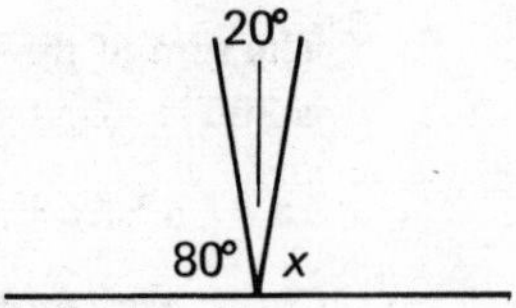

9

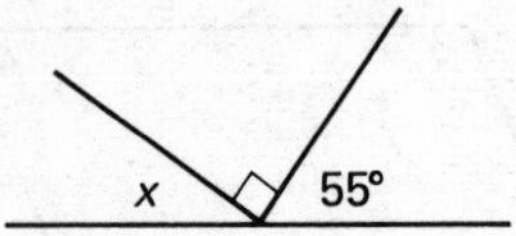

10

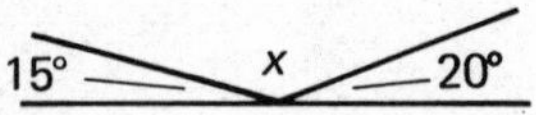

11

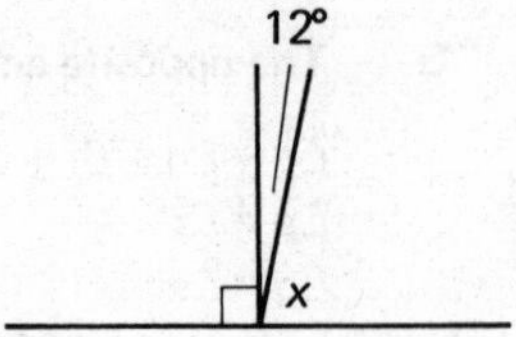

12

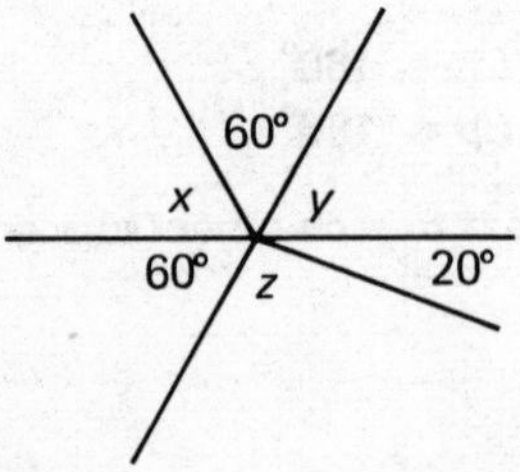

13

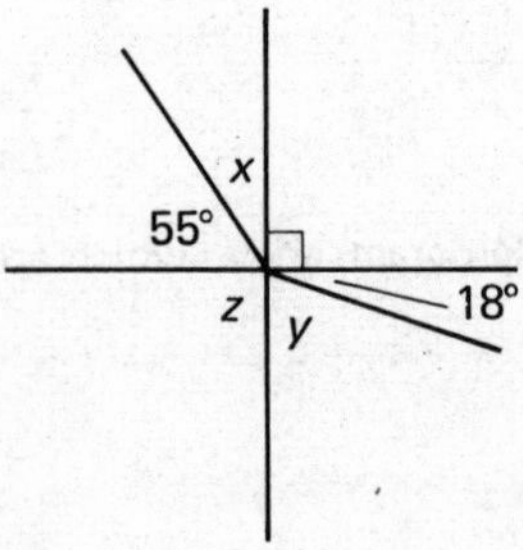

14

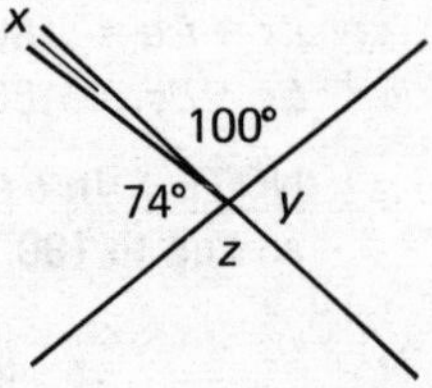

15

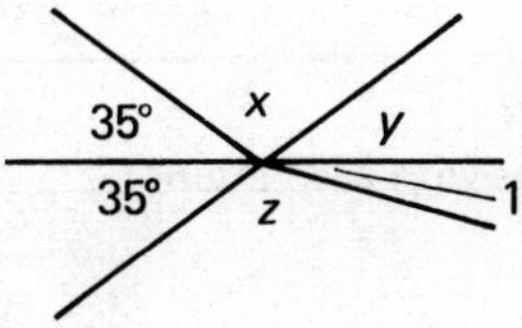

16

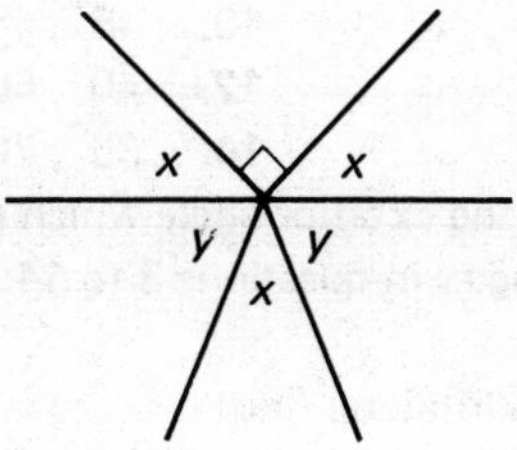

17

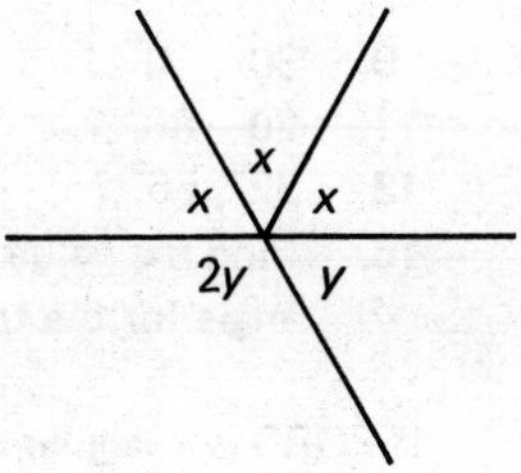

18

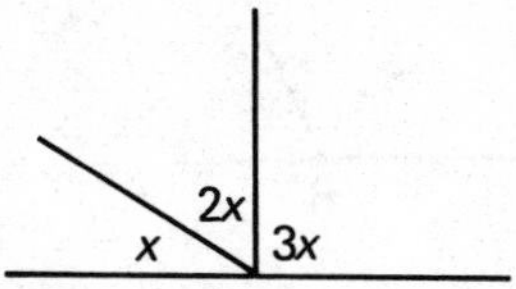

19

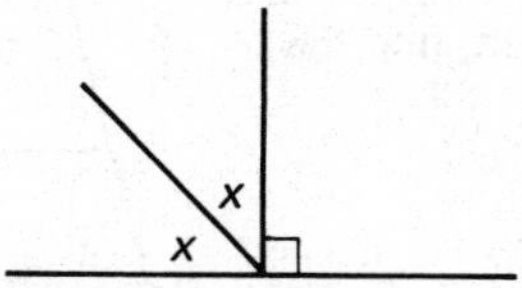

20

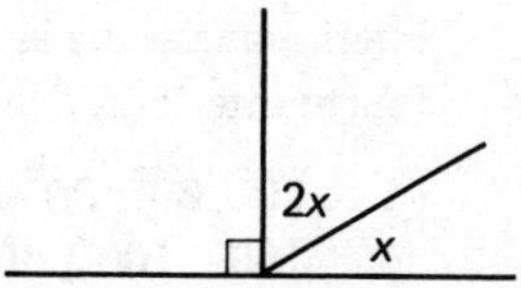

21

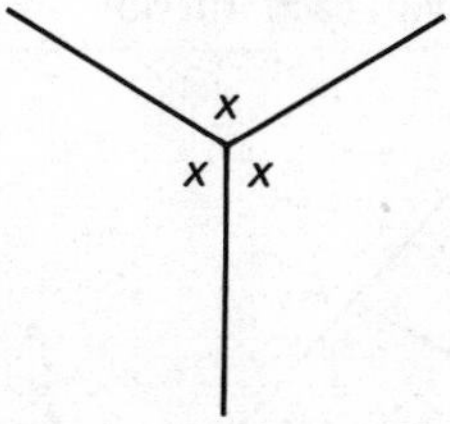

22

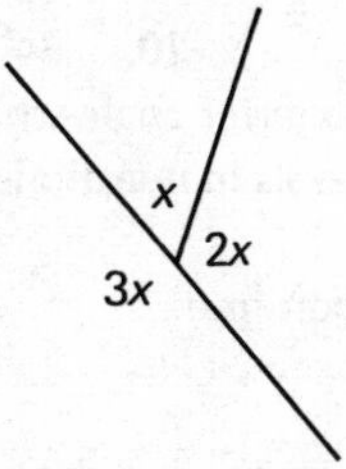

23

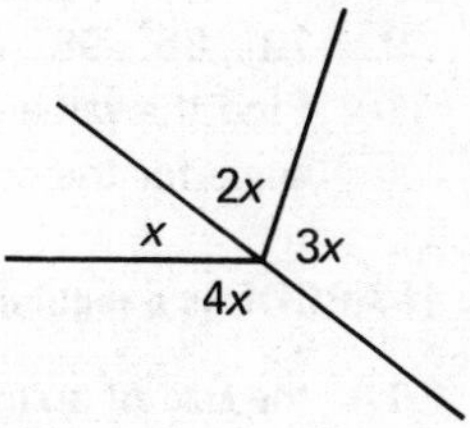

24

Exercise 54

A If $\triangle$ABC is **regular** find:

1. the size of an exterior $\angle$;

2. the size of an interior $\angle$;

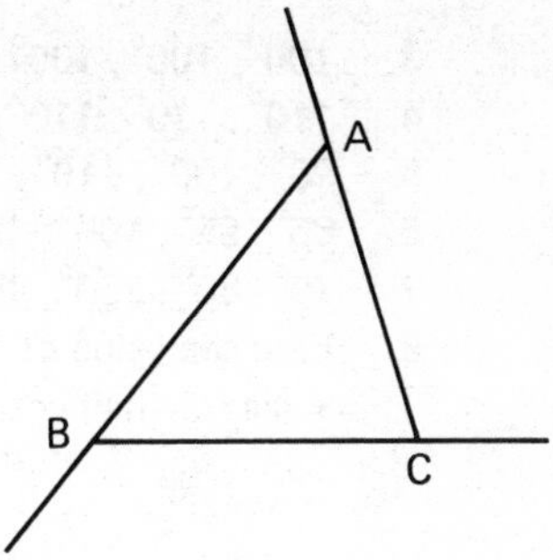

If $\triangle$ABC is **not regular** and two interior angles are as given, find the third interior $\angle$:

3. 40°, 50°,?

4. 30°, 60°,?

5. 20°, 70°,?

6. 45°, 45°,?

7. 25°, 25°,?

8. 50°, 50°,?

9. 30°, 30°,?
10. 48°, 48°,?
11. 20°, 80°,?
12. 40°, 60°,?
13. 32°, 56°,?
14. 36°, 76°,?
15. Find the value of the exterior angle which goes with each interior angle for the triangles in questions 3 to 14.

B If PQRS is a **regular** quadrilateral find:

1. the size of an exterior ∠;
2. the size of an interior ∠;

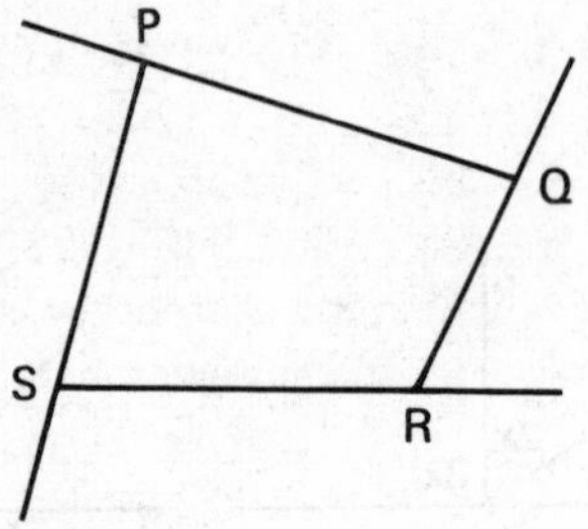

If PQRS is **not regular** and three interior angles are as given, find the fourth interior ∠:

3. 80°, 80°, 80°,?
4. 100°, 100°, 100°,?
5. 80°, 90°, 100°,?
6. 50°, 100°, 150°,?
7. 70°, 110°, 150°,?
8. 65°, 85°, 105°,?
9. 78°, 88°, 98°,?
10. 64°, 87°, 95°,?
11. Find the value of the exterior angle which goes with each interior angle for the quadrilaterals in questions 3 to 10.

C If ABCDE is a **regular** pentagon find:

1. the size of an exterior ∠;
2. the size of an interior ∠;

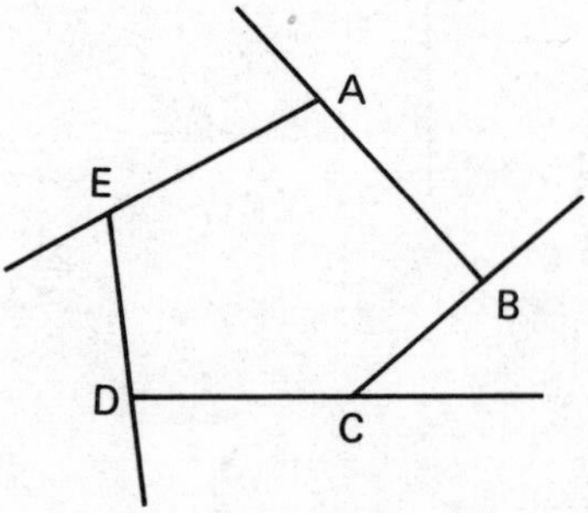

If ABCDE is **not regular** and four interior angles are as given, find the fifth interior ∠:

3. 100°, 100°, 100°, 100°,?
4. 110°, 110°, 110°, 110°,?
5. 90°, 100°, 110°, 120°,?
6. 85°, 95°, 105°, 115°,?
7. 70°, 80°, 150°, 160°,?
8. 74°, 85°, 93°, 158°,?
9. Find the value of the exterior angle which goes with each interior angle for the pentagons in questions 3 to 8.

D If PQRSTU is a **regular** hexagon find:

1. the size of an exterior ∠;
2. the size of an interior ∠;

If PQRSTU is **not regular** and five interior angles are as given, find the sixth interior ∠:

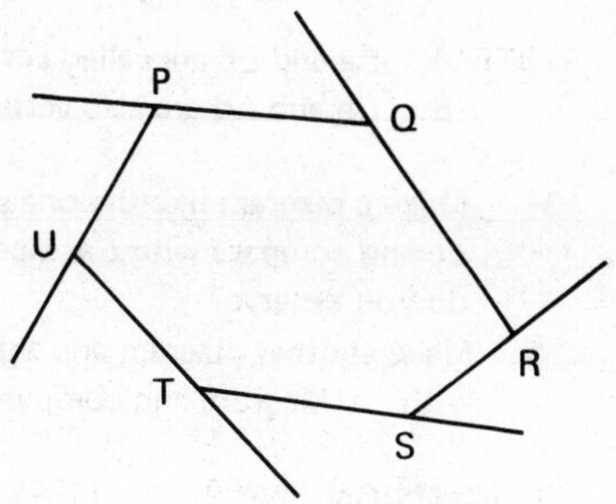

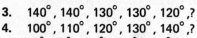

3. 140°, 140°, 130°, 130°, 120°,?
4. 100°, 110°, 120°, 130°, 140°,?
5. 90°, 90°, 135°, 135°, 135°,?
6. 96°, 105°, 118°, 123°, 132°,?
7. Find the value of the exterior angle which goes with each interior angle for the hexagons in questions 3 to 6.

E **1.** Find the size of an exterior angle of a regular octagon.
2. Find the size of an interior angle of a regular octagon.

If the exterior angles of a regular polygon are as given, find how many sides the polygon has:

3. Exterior ∠ = 30° **4.** Exterior ∠ = 40°
5. Exterior ∠ = 36° **6.** Exterior ∠ = 24°
7. Exterior ∠ = 20° **8.** Exterior ∠ = 18°

More facts about angles

Exercise 55

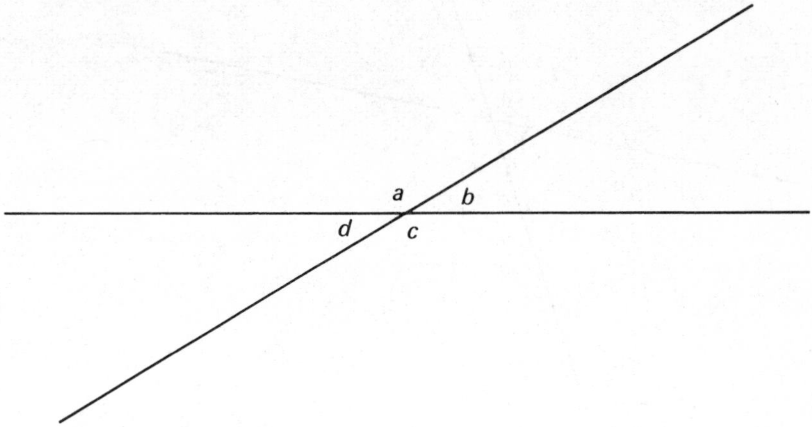

1 Measure ∠a and ∠c. What do you observe?
2 Measure ∠b and ∠d. What do you observe?

NOTE A $\angle a$ and $\angle c$ are called **vertically opposite angles.**
B $\angle b$ and $\angle d$ are also **vertically opposite angles.**

3 Make a diagram like the one shown on page 59 but let $\angle a = 140^\circ$. Measure $\angle c$ and compare with $\angle a$. Measure $\angle b$ and $\angle d$. Compare the results. What do you observe?

4 Make another diagram and this time let $\angle a = 60^\circ$. Measure $\angle c$ and compare with $\angle a$. Measure and compare $\angle b$ and $\angle d$. What do you observe?

CONCLUSION

Vertically opposite angles are equal

Exercise 56

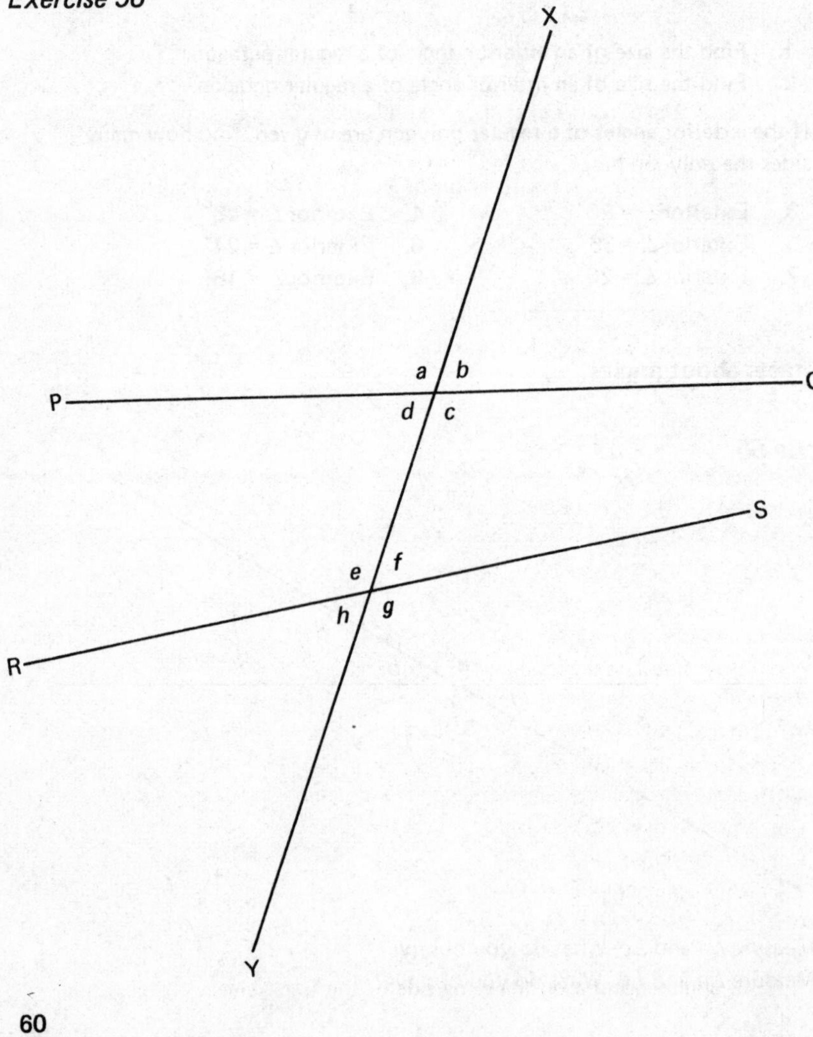

VOCABULARY

A straight line which cuts two or more other straight lines is called a **transversal. XY is a transversal.**

The angles *a, b, g, h* are called **exterior angles.**

The angles *c, d, e, f* are **interior angles.**

The angles *c* and *f* are called **interior angles on the same side of the transversal.** Angles *d* and *e* are also interior angles on the same side of the transversal.

The angles *d* and *f* are called **alternate angles.** Angles *c* and *e* are also alternate angles.

The angles *a* and *e* are called **corresponding angles**; so are angles *d* and *h*; so are angles *b* and *f*; so are angles *c* and *g*.

QUESTIONS

1 If $\angle a = 110^\circ$, what will be the size of $\angle c$, $\angle b$, $\angle d$? Measure them to make sure.

2 If $\angle e = 120^\circ$, what will be the size of $\angle g$, $\angle f$, $\angle h$? Measure them to make sure.

3 Make your own copy of this diagram using $\angle a = 130^\circ$ and PQ || RS (parallel). PQ and RS need to be each at least 11 cm long and XY at least 14 cm long to be able to use your protractor easily. Measure and note the value of each angle *a, b, c, d, e, f, g, h*. What do you observe about the following pairs of angles:

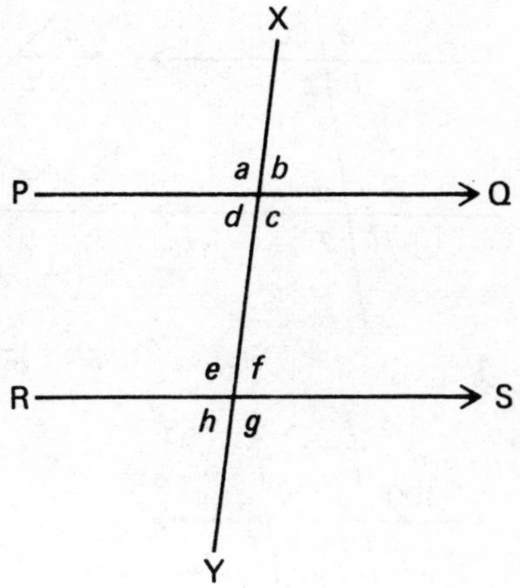

4 Vertically opposite angles *a* and *c*?

5 Vertically opposite angles *b* and *d*?

6 Vertically opposite angles *e* and *g*?

7 Vertically opposite angles *f* and *h*?

8 Alternate angles *d* and *f*?

9 Alternate angles *c* and *e*?

10 Corresponding angles *b* and *f*?

11 Corresponding angles *c* and *g*?

12 Corresponding angles *a* and *e*?

13 Corresponding angles *d* and *h*?

14 Interior angles *c* and *f* on the same side of the transversal - what is their sum?

15 Interior angles *d* and *e* on the same side of the transversal — what is their sum?

CONCLUSIONS When a transversal cuts a pair of **parallel** straight lines:

A **Alternate angles are equal**
B **Corresponding angles are equal**
C **The sum of interior angles on the same side of the transversal is 180°**

Exercise 57

Calculate the value of the lettered angles in the following diagrams:

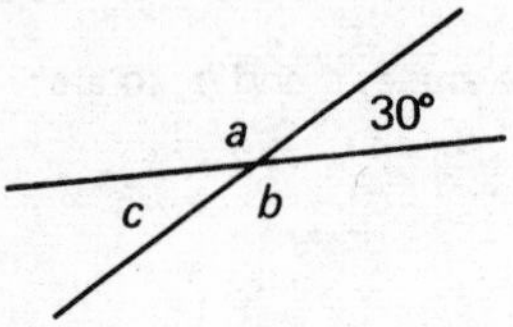

1

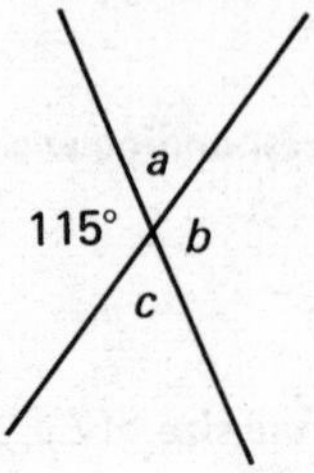

2

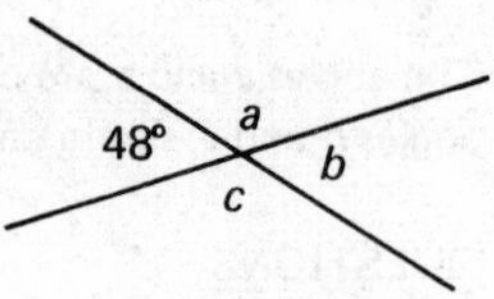

3

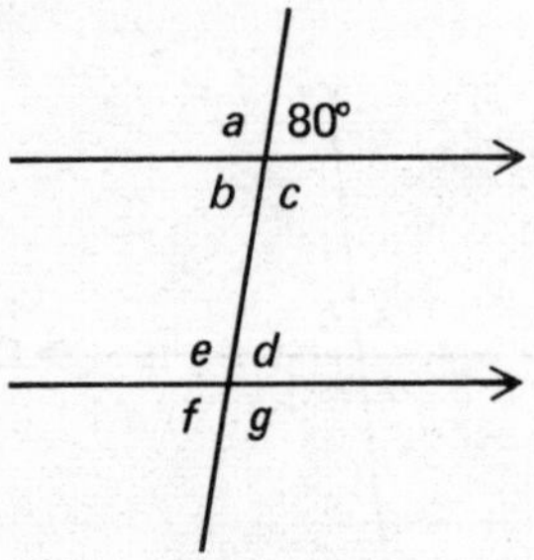

4

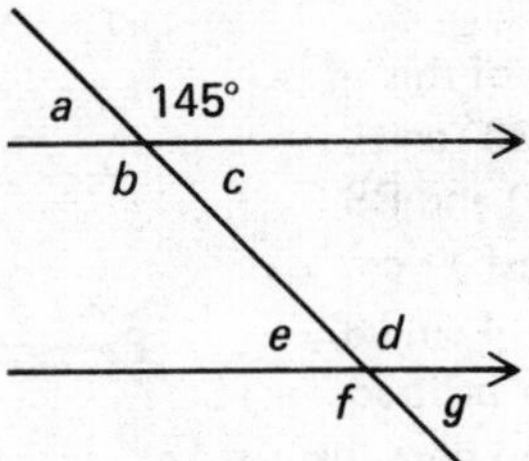

5

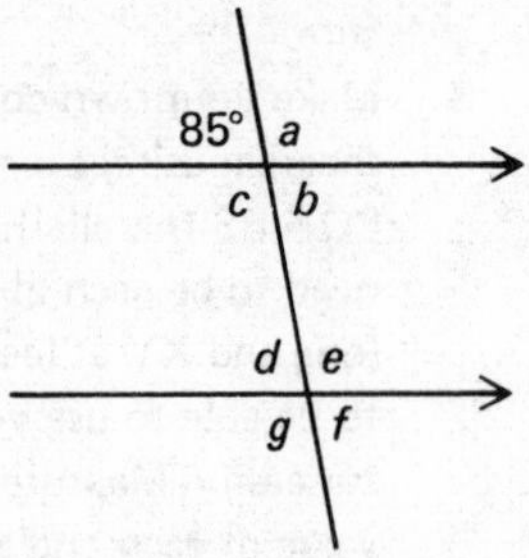

6

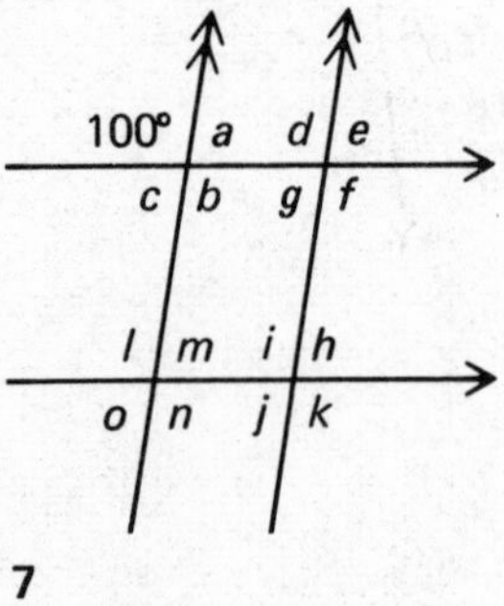

7

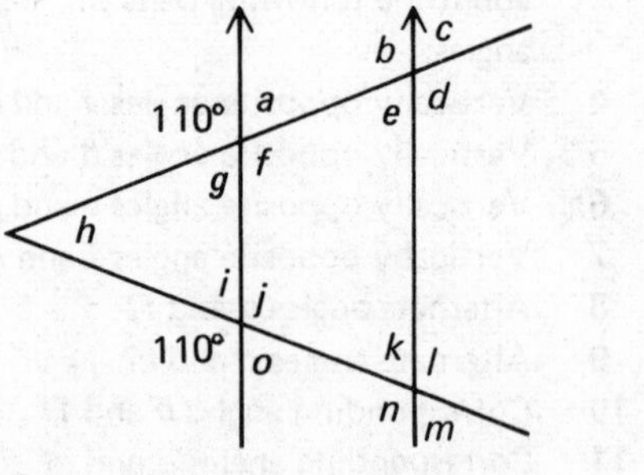

8

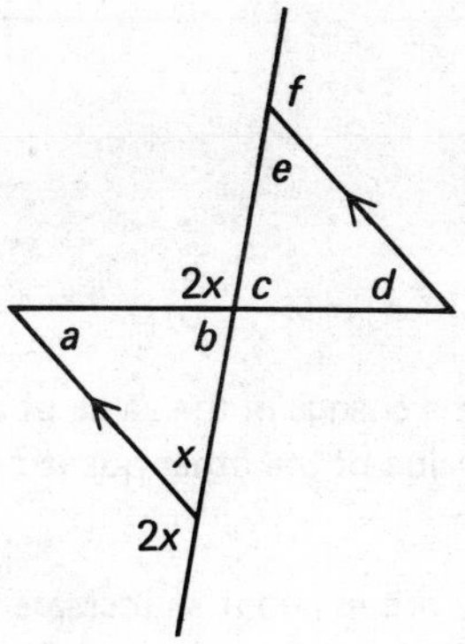

9

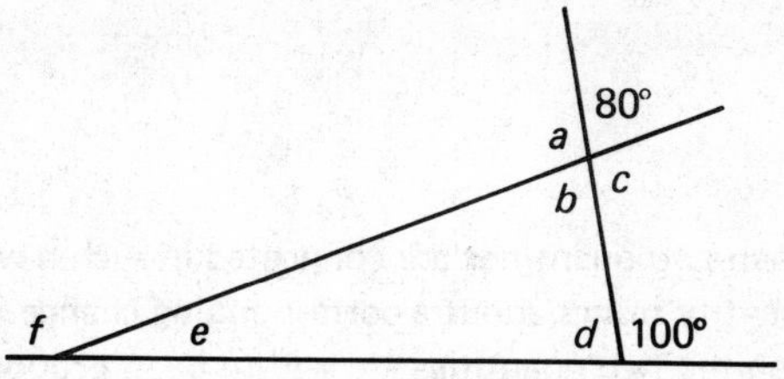

10

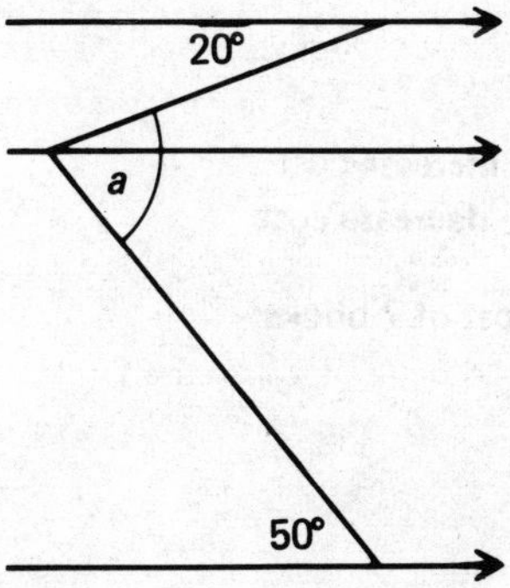

11

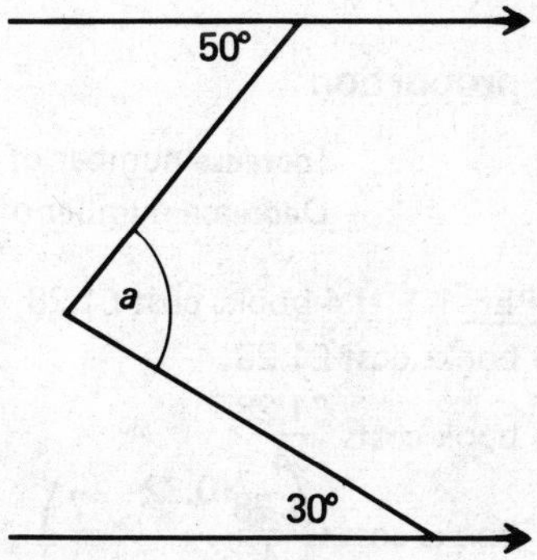

12

12 Proportion

When two quantities are connected in such a way that a change in the value of one quantity brings about a corresponding change in the value of the other quantity then the two quantities are said to be **in proportion.**

In many cases an **increase** in the value of one quantity brings about an **increase** in the value of the other, and if one **decreases** the other **decreases.**

Sometimes, however, the change can be the opposite way round – if one **increases** the other **decreases.**

Note the following examples:

Direct proportion

Increase number of articles – **increase** cost
Decrease number of articles – **decrease** cost

EXAMPLE 1 If 4 books cost £1.28, find the cost of 7 books

4 books cost £1.28

$\therefore$ 1 book costs $\frac{£1.28}{4}$

$\therefore$ 7 books cost £$\left(\frac{\cancel{1.28}^{0.32}}{\cancel{4}_1} \times \frac{7}{1}\right)$

= £0.32 × 7

Ans = £2.24

NOTE 7 books should cost **more** than 4 books.

EXAMPLE 2 If 16 articles cost £4, find the cost of 12 articles

16 articles cost £4

$\therefore$ 1 article costs $\frac{£4}{16}$

$\therefore$ 12 articles cost £$\left(\frac{\cancel{4}^{1}}{\cancel{16}_{\cancel{4}_1}} \times \frac{\cancel{12}^{3}}{1}\right)$

Ans = £3

NOTE 12 articles should cost **less** than 16 articles

Inverse proportion

Consider a group of men working to finish a job in a given time:

Increase the number of men – **decrease** the time
Decrease the number of men – **increase** the time

NOTE   This might suggest that if we increased the number of men building a house then, if the number of men was large enough, the house could be built in, say, ten minutes. Clearly, this would be impossible – so many men would get in each other's way and they would be unable to carry out their own special tasks.

EXAMPLE 3   If it requires 4 days for 10 men to dig a trench, find how long it will take 8 men.

10 men take 4 days

$\therefore$ 1 man takes (4×10) days

$\therefore$ 8 men take $\left(\frac{4 \times 10}{8}\right)$ days

Ans = 5 days

NOTE   8 men will take **more** time than 10 men

EXAMPLE 4   A ship has sufficient food to feed 900 people for 4 weeks. How long will the food last for 1200 people?

900 people have food for 4 weeks

$\therefore$ 1 person has food for (900×4) weeks

$\therefore$ 1200 people have food for $\left(\frac{900 \times 4}{1200}\right)$ weeks

Ans = 3 weeks

NOTE

1 1200 people will eat more food than 900 people so a given quantity of food will last **less** time.
2 Consider each problem carefully and decide whether the quantity to be found will **increase or decrease.**
3 Arrange the information from the question in the form of a sentence. Place the quantity which forms the answer **at the end of the sentence.**
   The sentence in Example 1 ended with **£s** not books.
   The sentence in Example 2 ended with **£s** not articles.

The sentence in Example 3 ended with **days** not men.
The sentence in Example 4 ended with **weeks** not people.

Exercise 58

1. If 6 books cost £3.60, find the cost of 8 books.
2. If 5 books cost £4.50, find the cost of 9 books.
3. If 8 articles cost £5.68, find the cost of 11 articles.
4. If 12 articles cost £18.48, find the cost of 20 articles.
5. If 7 books cost £3.50, find the cost of 4 books.
6. If 9 books cost £5.58, find the cost of 5 books.
7. If 12 articles cost £26.64, find the cost of 7 articles.
8. If 18 articles cost £37.80, find the cost of 12 articles.
9. If 7 dozen articles cost £3.50, find the cost of 9 dozen.
10. If 8 dozen articles cost £3.20, find the cost of 5 dozen.
11. If 130 articles cost £2.86, find the cost of 70 articles.
12. If 240 articles cost £14.40, find the cost of 300 articles.
13. If 9 metres of ribbon cost £2.52, find the cost of 6 metres.
14. If 7 metres of cloth cost £16.45, find the cost of 10 metres.
15. If $2\frac{1}{2}$ metres of cloth cost £14.20, find the cost of $5\frac{1}{4}$ metres.
16. If 2 tonnes of coal cost £85.44, find the cost of $3\frac{1}{4}$ tonnes.
17. If $3\frac{1}{2}$ tonnes of chemical cost £93.24, find the cost of $2\frac{1}{3}$ tonnes.
18. If $4\frac{1}{4}$ tonnes of chemical cost £51, find the cost of $3\frac{1}{3}$ tonnes.
19. If 6 men build a wall in 10 days, find how long it will take 4 men.
20. If 8 men build a wall in 3 days, find how long it will take 6 men.
21. If 10 men build a wall in 7 days, find how long it will take 7 men.
22. If 6 men dig a trench in 6 days, find how long it will take 9 men.
23. If 40 men complete a job in 21 days, find how long it will take 56 men.
24. If 24 men complete a job in 39 days, find how long it will take 36 men.
25. If 18 men complete a job in 17 days, find how long it will take 34 men.
26. If 4 pipes empty a bath in 1 hour, how long will it take 2 pipes?
27. If 1 tap fills a bath in 30 min, how long will it take 2 taps?
28. 6 pipes empty a bath in 1 h 20 min. How long will it take if only 5 pipes are used?
29. 4 taps fill a bath in 2 h 30 min. How long will it take 5 taps?
30. A garrison has sufficient food to last 1000 soldiers for 21 days. How long will the food last for 1400 soldiers?

13 Ratio

Ratio is a method of comparing two or more quantities. If we are told that a class of 30 pupils contains 20 boys and 10 girls, we may say: 'There are twice as many boys in the class as there are girls.'

This same information can be given in the following way:

The **ratio** of the number of boys to the number of girls is 2 to 1 (20 to 10 in its simplest form).

The **ratio** 2 to 1 is written **2 : 1** or as a fraction $\frac{2}{1}$.

The **ratio** of the number of girls to the number of boys is 1 to 2 (10 to 20), this is written **1 : 2**
or as a fraction $\frac{1}{2}$.

<u>NOTE</u>

1 When the answer to a question is in the form of a ratio, the answer **MUST** contain the ratio as a statement in words as well as figures.

In a simple form: Boys to girls = 2:1
or: Girls to boys = 1:2

The figures must be in the same order as the words.

2 The ratio should be in its simplest form:

6 : 4 = 3 : 2 or 1½ : 1

Exercise 59

Express the first quantity as a ratio of the second. Give the answer as simply as possible: (a) in the form x : y ; (b) as a fraction.

1. 12 ; 3	**2.** 3 ; 12	**3.** 5 ; 15	**4.** 15 ; 5
5. 25 ; 5	**6.** 5 ; 25	**7.** 6 ; 18	**8.** 18 ; 6
9. 4 ; 24	**10.** 24 ; 4	**11.** 36 ; 9	**12.** 9 ; 36
13. 12 ; 24	**14.** 36 ; 12	**15.** 18 ; 36	**16.** 36 ; 4
17. 24 ; 18	**18.** 24 ; 36	**19.** 36 ; 48	**20.** 48 ; 56

21. £2.50 ; £10	**22.** £7.50 ; £5	**23.** £15 ; £42
24. £3 ; £2.10	**25.** £12 ; £16	**26.** £450 ; £200
27. 25 min ; 1¼ h	**28.** 2h 20min ; 50min	**29.** Feb ; Sept

30 George earns £3600 a year, Henry earns £4500 a year. What is the ratio of George's income to Henry's income?

31 Anne saves £450 a year, Betty saves £550 a year. What is the ratio of Betty's savings to Anne's savings?

32 A school contains 250 girls, 300 boys. Find the ratio of: (a) the number of girls to the number of boys; (b) the number of boys to the number of girls; (c) the number of girls to the **total** number of pupils.

Increase and decrease in a given ratio

On page 64 , in Example 1, we see that the cost of 4 books (£1.28) increases when 7 books are purchased. We can say: **New Quantity : Original Quantity = 7 : 4**

$\therefore$ **Original cost has increased in the ratio 7 : 4**

We can work out the new cost by using the ratio 7:4 as a **multiplying fraction:**

$$\text{New cost} = \text{Original cost} \times \frac{7}{4}$$

$$= \pounds\,\frac{\cancel{1{\cdot}28}^{\,0{\cdot}32}}{1} \times \frac{7}{\cancel{4}_{\,1}}$$

$$\text{Ans} = \underline{\pounds 2.24}$$

On page 64, in Example 2, we see the cost of 16 articles (£4) decreases when 12 articles are purchased. We can say: **New Quantity : Original Quantity = 12 : 16.**

$\therefore$ **Original cost has decreased in the ratio 12 : 16**

We can work out the new cost by using the ratio 12:16 as a **multiplying fraction:**

$$\text{New cost} = \text{Original cost} \times \frac{12}{16}$$

$$= \pounds\,\frac{\cancel{4}^{\,1}}{1} \times \frac{12}{\cancel{16}_{\,4}}$$

$$= \pounds\,\frac{\cancel{12}^{\,3}}{\cancel{4}_{\,1}}$$

$$\text{Ans} = \underline{\pounds 3}$$

<u>NOTE</u>

1 Think carefully to decide whether the **quantity to be found** increases or decreases.

2 For an **increase** the multiplying fraction must have the **larger number on top.**
3 For a **decrease** the multiplying fraction must have the **smaller number on top.**

Exercise 60

1 Increase 12 in the ratio 4:3
2 Increase 16 in the ratio 5:4
3 Increase 20 in the ratio 6:5
4 Increase 30 in the ratio 7:6
5 Increase 40 in the ratio 9:8
6 Increase 45 in the ratio 10:9
7 Increase 60 in the ratio 11:10
8 Increase 72 in the ratio 13:12
9 Increase 84 in the ratio 15:14
10 Increase 96 in the ratio 17:16
11 Decrease 8 in the ratio 3:4
12 Decrease 20 in the ratio 4:5
13 Decrease 24 in the ratio 5:6
14 Decrease 28 in the ratio 6:7
15 Decrease 32 in the ratio 7:8
16 Decrease 36 in the ratio 8:9
17 Decrease 60 in the ratio 9:10
18 Decrease 90 in the ratio 13:15
19 Decrease 91 in the ratio 12:13
20 Decrease 102 in the ratio 15:17
21 Increase 2¼kg in the ratio 4:3
22 Increase £2.40 in the ratio 7:6
23 Increase $3\frac{1}{3}$m in the ratio 8:5
24 Increase 1½ days in the ratio 14:9
25 Decrease $5\frac{5}{8}$kg in the ratio 8:9
26 Decrease £1.12 in the ratio 15:28
27 Decrease 33m in the ratio 7:11
28 Decrease 8h 45min in the ratio 4:5
29 What multiplying fraction changes 50 into 25?
30 What multiplying fraction changes 2m into 4m?
31 What multiplying fraction changes 10 litres into 15 litres?
32 What multiplying fraction changes 45kg into 30kg?
33 In what ratio must 60 be increased to become 75?
34 In what ratio must 84 be decreased to become 72?
35 In what ratio must 96 be increased to become 120?
36 In what ratio must 112 be decreased to become 84?
37 The price of an article changes from 48p to 42p. In what ratio has the price changed?

38 The price of an article changes from 88p to £1.43. In what ratio has the price changed?

39 If 7kg of grass seed cost £3.36, find the cost of 5kg.

40 The wages bill for 50 men is £825, find the bill for 36 men.

Sharing in a given ratio

EXAMPLE 1 Share £120 in the ratio 3 : 2 : 1

Total number of parts = 3 + 2 + 1 = 6

$\therefore$ Value of one part = £ $\frac{120}{6}$ = £20

Value of first share = £20 X 3 = £60
Value of second share = £20 X 2 = £40
Value of third share = £20 X 1 = £20

Ans = £60; £40; £20

CHECK The three shares should add up to £120. Do they?

EXAMPLE 2 Share £126 so that A has three times as much as B, who has twice as much as C.

If C's share is 1 part
then B's share is 2 parts (*twice as much as C*)
and A's share is 6 parts (*three times as much as B*)

Total number of parts = 1 + 2 + 6 = 9

$\therefore$ Value of one part = £ $\frac{126}{9}$ = £14

C's share (1 part) = £14
B's share (2 parts) = £14 X 2 = £28
A's share (6 parts) = £14 X 6 = £84

Ans = A's share £84; B's share £28; C's share £14

CHECK The three shares should add up to £126. Do they?

Exercise 61

1. Share 6 in the ratio 1:2:3
2. Share 18 in the ratio 3:2:1
3. Share 25 in the ratio 2:3
4. Share 28 in the ratio 3:4

5 Share £27 in the ratio 1:3:5

6 Share £35 in the ratio 1:2:4

7 Share £48 in the ratio 3:4:5

8 Share 15 hours in the ratio 2:3

9 Share 36 hours in the ratio 7:5

10 Share 1½ hours in the ratio 7:10:13

11 Share 112kg in the ratio 5:10:13

12 Share 45 litres in the ratio 3:5:7

13 Share £15 in the ratio 4:2:1:½

14 Share £30 in the ratio 1½:2¼:3¾

15 Share £13 in the ratio $\frac{1}{2}:\frac{1}{3}:\frac{1}{4}$

16 Share £54 so that A has three times as much as B, who has twice as much as C.

17 Share £117 so that C has three times as much as B, who has twice as much as A.

18 Share £63 so that B has three times as much as A, who has twice as much as C.

19 Share £84 so that A has twice as much as B, who has twice as much as C.

20 Share £112 so that C has twice as much as B, who has twice as much as A.

21 Share £140 so that C has half as much as B, who has half as much as A.

22 Share £50 so that A has £10 more than B.

23 Share £60 so that A has £10 more than B, who has twice as much as C.

24 Share £60 so that A has £10 more than B, who has £10 more than C.

14 Percentage changes

Increase

If a quantity increases by 20%, it means that every 100 parts of the original are now worth 120 parts. Thus £100 will increase to £120. The ratio of the **new value to the old** (120:100) can be written as a fraction 120/100 and used as a **multiplying fraction.**

EXAMPLE 1 Increase £30 by 20%

Old value	=	100%	=	£30
Increase	=	20%		
New value	=	120%		
Multiplying fraction	=	$\frac{120}{100}$		

$$\text{New value} = £\,\frac{30}{1} \times \frac{\cancel{120}^{\,6}}{\cancel{100}_{\,5}}$$

$$= £\,\frac{\cancel{30}^{\,6}}{1} \times \frac{6}{\cancel{5}_{\,1}}$$

$$\text{Ans} = \underline{£36}$$

NOTE For an **increase** the multiplying fraction must have the **larger number on top.**

Decrease

If a quantity decreases by 20%, it means that every 100 parts of the original are now worth 80 parts. Thus £100 will decrease to £80. The ratio of the **new value to the old** (80:100) can be written as a fraction 80/100 and used as a **multiplying fraction.**

EXAMPLE 2 Decrease £30 by 20%

Old value = 100% = £30
Decrease = 20%
New value = 80%

Multiplying fraction = $\frac{80}{100}$

New value = $£\ \frac{30}{1} \times \frac{\cancel{80}^{4}}{\cancel{100}_{5}}$

= $£\ \frac{\cancel{30}^{6}}{1} \times \frac{4}{\cancel{5}_{1}}$

Ans = £24

NOTE For a **decrease** the multiplying fraction must have the **smaller number on top.**

Exercise 62

Find the required **multiplying fraction** (*cancelled to lowest terms*) to increase a quantity by:

1. 5%	**2.** 10%	**3.** 15%	**4.** 20%	**5.** 25%
6. 30%	**7.** 35%	**8.** 40%	**9.** 45%	**10.** 50%
11. 55%	**12.** 60%	**13.** 65%	**14.** 70%	**15.** 75%
16. 80%	**17.** 85%	**18.** 90%	**19.** 95%	**20.** 100%
21. 6%	**22.** 18%	**23.** 36%	**24.** 12½%	**25.** 37½%

Exercise 63

Find the required **multiplying fraction** (*cancelled to lowest terms*) to decrease a quantity by:

1. 5%	**2.** 10%	**3.** 15%	**4.** 20%	**5.** 25%
6. 30%	**7.** 35%	**8.** 40%	**9.** 45%	**10.** 50%
11. 55%	**12.** 60%	**13.** 65%	**14.** 70%	**15.** 75%
16. 80%	**17.** 85%	**18.** 90%	**19.** 95%	**20.** 99%
21. 1%	**22.** 6%	**23.** 18%	**24.** 12½%	**25.** 37½%

Exercise 64

1	Increase 20 by 20%	2	Increase 30 by 30%
3	Increase 40 by 40%	4	Increase 50 by 50%
5	Increase 60 by 60%	6	Increase 70 by 70%
7	Increase £80 by 80%	8	Increase £90 by 90%
9	Increase £160 by 20%	10	Increase £240 by 25%
11	Decrease 10 by 10%	12	Decrease 20 by 20%
13	Decrease 30 by 30%	14	Decrease 40 by 40%
15	Decrease 50 by 50%	16	Decrease 60 by 60%
17	Decrease £70 by 70%	18	Decrease £80 by 80%
19	Decrease £60 by 10%	20	Decrease £120 by 25%
21	Increase £80 by 40%	22	Increase £128 by 75%
23	Decrease £96 by 25%	24	Decrease £60 by 15%

Exercise 65

From the catalogue, calculate 10% of the price of each of the following items:

1.	CB 3	2.	CB 15	3.	CG 2	4.	CM 2
5.	CM 20	6.	CW 3	7.	CW 12	8.	F 2
9.	CW 4	10.	CM 18	11.	CW 10	12.	CG 13
13.	CM 3	14.	CB 4	15.	CW 17	16.	F 5
17.	CG 3	18.	F 3	19.	CM 9	20.	F 6
21.	F 10	22.	HW 1	23.	L 3	24.	L 5
25.	HW 2	26.	F 7	27.	F 11	28.	HW 24
29.	HW 5	30.	L 10	31.	HW 13	32.	F 15
33.	F 12	34.	HW 15	35.	F 18	36.	HW 3

Exercise 66

Increase the catalogue price of the following items by 8%: (*Value added tax = VAT*)

1.	CB 1	2.	CB 2	3.	CB 3	4.	CB 9
5.	CB 11	6.	CB 13	7.	CB 16	8.	CB 5
9.	CG 2	10.	CG 9	11.	CM 3	12.	CM 4
13.	CM 5	14.	CM 7	15.	CM 13	16.	CM 14
17.	CM 16	18.	CW 4	19.	CW 14	20.	F 1

15 Graphs

Straight-line graphs

The idea of **proportion** (*when the change in one quantity is related to the change in a second quantity*) can be illustrated by graphs.

EXAMPLE If 10kg of potatoes cost 75p, draw a graph to show the relationship between **Quantity in kilograms** and **Cost in pence.**

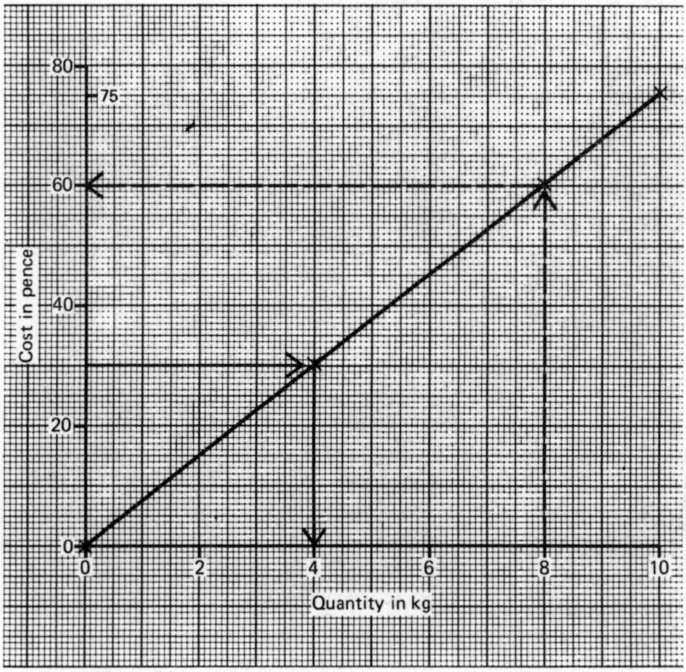

NOTE To draw the graph line, it is necessary first to plot two points:

1 where 0kg cost 0 pence, **2** where 10kg cost 75 pence.

QUESTIONS

Use the graph to find:
1 the cost of 8kg of potatoes,
2 the quantity which can be bought for 30p.

Exercise 67

1 Make your own copy of the graph on page 75 and use it it find:
- (a) the cost of 6kg of potatoes,
- (b) the quantity which can be bought for 15p,
- (c) the cost of 9kg of potatoes,
- (d) the quantity which can be bought for 22½p.

2 An advertisement in an orchard tells you that you may pick your own apples for the price of 50 pence for 10kg. Draw a graph to show the relationship between Quantity and Cost. The **small graph** at the right shows the axes to help you.

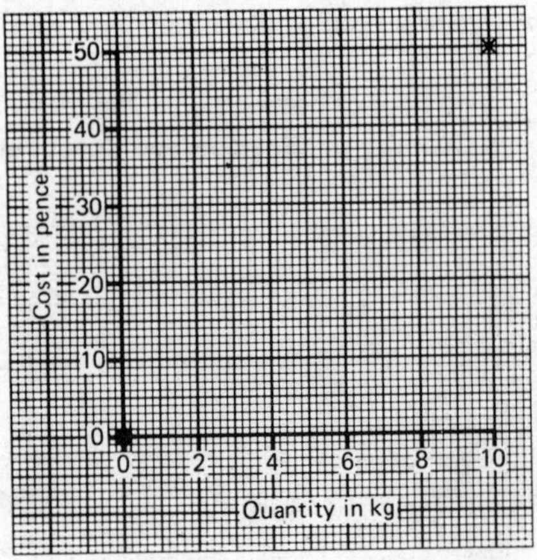

Use your graph to find:
- (a) the cost of 2kg; 5kg; 9kg,
- (b) the quantity which can be bought for 40p; 35p; 15p.

3 Ten metres of curtain material cost £25. Draw a graph to show the relationship between Quantity and Cost.

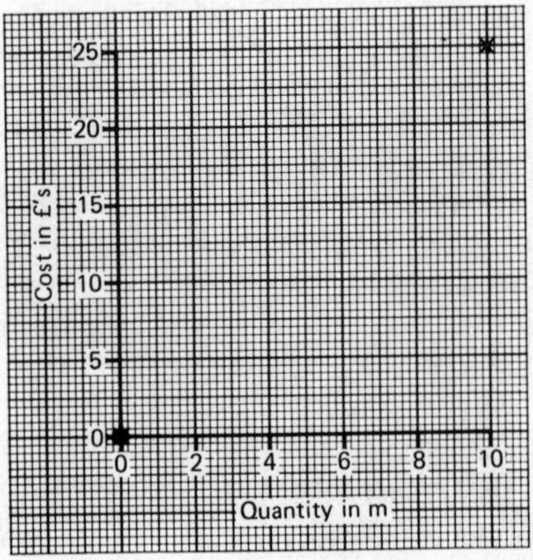

Use your graph to find:
- (a) the cost of 6m; 9m; 3½m,
- (b) the quantity which can be bought for £5; £17.50; £11.25.

4 Four litres of cleaning fluid cost 80 pence. Draw a graph to show the relationship between Quantity and Cost.
Use your graph to find:
(a) the cost of 1 litre; 3½ litres,
(b) the quantity which can be bought for 60p; 25p.

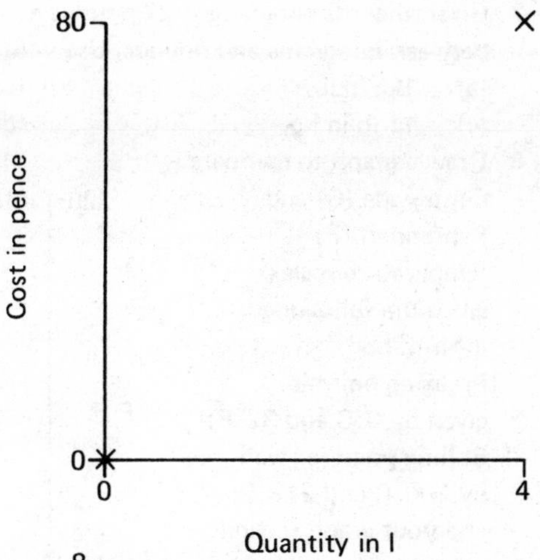

5 Given that 8km = 5 miles, draw a graph to show the relationship between kilometres and miles.
Use your graph to estimate:
(a) 4km in miles,
(b) 5km in miles,
(c) 1¼ miles in km,
(d) 3 miles in km.

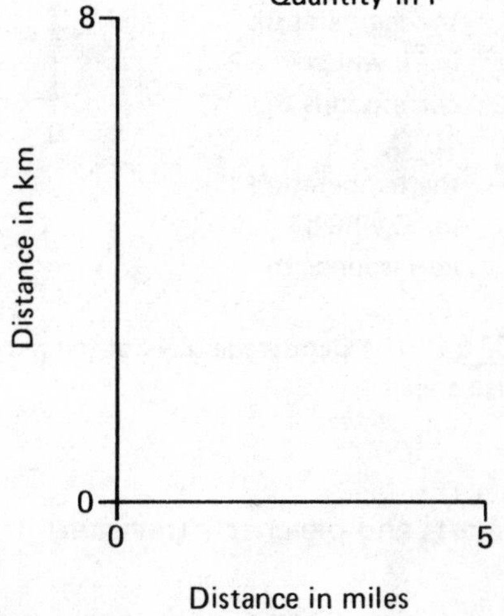

6 Given that 4 litres = 7 pints, draw a graph to show the relationship between litres and pints.
Use your graph to estimate.
(a) 1 litre in pints,
(b) 3·5 litres in pints,
(c) 1 pint in litres,
(d) 3·5 pints in litres.

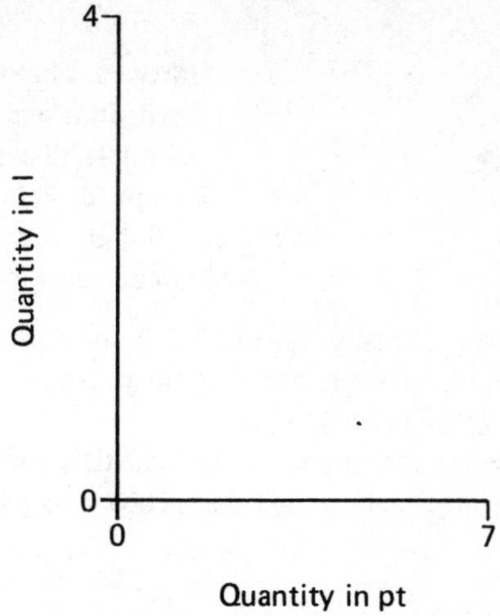

7 Given that 10 kilograms = 22 pounds, draw a graph to show the relationship between kilograms and pounds. Use your graph to estimate:

(a) 1kg in lb, (b) 7·5 kg in lb,
(c) 11 lb in kg, (d) 18 lb in kg.

8 Draw a graph to compare Centigrade (C) and Fahrenheit (F) temperature scales given the following information:
Freezing point is given by 0°C and 32°F;
Boiling point is given by 100°C and 212°F.
Use your graph to find:

(a) the temperature in °F which corresponds to 10°C,
(b) the temperature in °C which corresponds to 140°F.

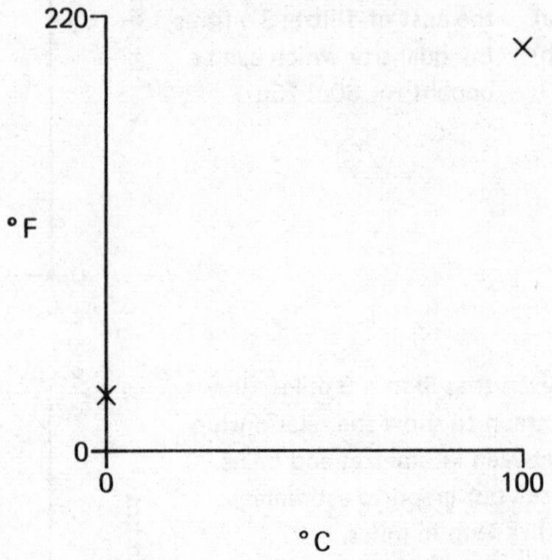

NOTE The **Centigrade** scale of temperature is often referred to as the **Celsius** scale.

Bar-charts and pie-charts (revision)

Exercise 68

Thirty days hath September,
April, June and November.
All the rest have thirty-one
Except for February alone,
Which hath but twenty-eight days clear
And twenty-nine in each leap year.

1 Draw up a tally-sheet to help you count the number of times each of the following letters occurs in the poem:

a; e; i; o; u; h; r; t

2 Use the information from your tally-sheet to draw a **bar-chart** to illustrate the information. Call the vertical axis **frequency**.

3 Use the information from your tally-sheet to draw a **pie-chart** to illustrate the information:

1 The total number of times the eight letters occur in the poem is 90.

2 Express the number of times the letter 'a' appears (15) as a fraction of the total (90).

3 Find the fraction of 360° to give the angle at the centre of the pie-chart:

$$\frac{15}{90} \times \frac{360^\circ}{1} = 60^\circ$$

4 Repeat this calculation for the remaining seven letters.

5 Draw a circle of about 6cm radius. Measure the angles, each in turn, at the centre of the circle.

6 Shade the *slices of the pie* in different colours to show the letter each slice represents.

16 More work with directed numbers

REMEMBER The Rule of Signs

+ (+)	means	+	Like signs give **plus**
− (−)	means	+	
+ (−)	means	−	Unlike signs give **minus**
− (+)	means	−	

Exercise 69 (revision)

1. 4 − 2	**2.** 4 + 2	**3.** 4 − (+ 2)
4. 4 + (+ 2)	**5.** 4 − (−2)	**6.** 4 + (−2)
7. 6 + (+ 3)	**8.** 6 − (+ 3)	**9.** 6 − (−3)
10. 6 + (−3)	**11.** 8 + (−4)	**12.** 8 − (−4)
13. 8 + (+ 4)	**14.** 8 − (+ 4)	**15.** 10 − (+ 5)
16. 10 + (−5)	**17.** 10 − (−5)	**18.** 10 + (+ 5)
19. (−2) + (+ 2)	**20.** (−2) − (−2)	**21.** (−2) + (−2)
22. (−2) − (+ 2)	**23.** (−5) − (−5)	**24.** (−5) + (−5)
25. (−5) − (+ 5)	**26.** (−5) + (+ 5)	**27.** (−9) − (+ 6)
28. (−9) − (−6)	**29.** (−9) + (+ 6)	**30.** (−9) + (−6)

Multiplication of directed numbers

EXAMPLE 1 (+ 10) × (+ 2) = + 20

STEPS: + times + gives +; 10 times 2 gives 20

EXAMPLE 2 (− 8) × (− 3) = + 24

STEPS: − times − gives +; 8 times 3 gives 24

EXAMPLE 3 (+ 6) × (− 5) = − 30

STEPS: + times − gives −; 6 times 5 gives 30

EXAMPLE 4 (− 7) × (+ 4) = − 28

STEPS; − times + gives −; 7 times 4 gives 28

Exercise 70

Write down the values of the following:

1.	(−2) X (+ 2)	**2.**	(+ 2) X (−2)	**3.**	(−2) X (−2)
4.	(+ 2) X (+ 2)	**5.**	(+ 3) X (−3)	**6.**	(−3) X (−3)
7.	(−3) X (+ 3)	**8.**	(+ 3) X (+ 3)	**9.**	(−3) X (+ 9)
10.	(+ 4) X (−7)	**11.**	(−4) X (−9)	**12.**	(+ 3) X (+ 7)
13.	(−4) X (−8)	**14.**	(−6) X (+ 3)	**15.**	(+ 5) X (−4)
16.	(−5) X (+ 7)	**17.**	(−8) X (−5)	**18.**	(−5) X (+ 9)
19.	(+ 7) X (+ 9)	**20.**	(+ 8) X (−7)	**21.**	(−7) X (+ 6)
22.	(−6) X (−9)	**23.**	(−7) X (−7)	**24.**	(+ 8) X (−9)
25.	(−6) X (+ 8)	**26.**	(+ 7) X (+ 12)	**27.**	(−9) X (+ 9)
28.	(+ 11) X (−11)	**29.**	(−11) X (+ 12)	**30.**	(−12) X (−9)

Exercise 71

Complete the following multiplication table:

	−4	−3	−2	−1	0	+1	+2	+3	+4
+4	−16				0				+16
+3									
+2									
+1									
0					0				
−1									
−2									
−3									
−4	+16								−16

Exercise 72

Complete the following table:

Values of "x"	−3	−2	−1	0	+1	+2	+3
$3x =$							
$-5x =$							
$x^2 =$							
$-x^3 =$							
$(-x)^3 =$							

Division of directed numbers

NOTE Read the sign ÷ as *divided by*.

EXAMPLE 1 (+ 20) ÷ (+ 10) = + 2

STEPS: + divided by + gives + ; 20 divided by 10 gives 2

EXAMPLE 2 (− 16) ÷ (−4) = + 4

STEPS: − divided by − gives + ; 16 divided by 4 gives 4

EXAMPLE 3 (+ 15) ÷ (−5) = −3

STEPS: + divided by − gives − ; 15 divided by 5 gives 3

EXAMPLE 4 (−30) ÷ (+ 6) = −5

STEPS: − divided by + gives − ; 30 divided by 6 gives 5

Exercise 73

1. (−3) ÷ (+ 3)	**2.** (+ 3) ÷ (−3)	**3.** (−3) ÷ (−3)
4. (+ 3) ÷ (+ 3)	**5.** (+ 4) ÷ (−4)	**6.** (−4) ÷ (−4)
7. (−4) ÷ (+ 4)	**8.** (+ 4) ÷ (+ 4)	**9.** (−9) ÷ (+ 3)
10. (+ 15) ÷ (−3)	**11.** (− 16) ÷ (−2)	**12.** (+ 16) ÷ (+ 8)
13. (− 18) ÷ (−6)	**14.** (− 18) ÷ (+ 2)	**15.** (+ 21) ÷ (−7)

16.	$(-24) \div (+3)$	**17.**	$(-24) \div (-6)$	**18.**	$(-24) \div (+12)$
19.	$(+25) \div (+5)$	**20.**	$(+27) \div (-9)$	**21.**	$(-28) \div (+4)$
22.	$(-30) \div (-15)$	**23.**	$(-32) \div (-8)$	**24.**	$(+33) \div (-3)$
25.	$(-35) \div (+7)$	**26.**	$(+36) \div (+4)$	**27.**	$(-40) \div (+5)$
28.	$(+42) \div (-6)$	**29.**	$(-45) \div (+9)$	**30.**	$(-49) \div (-7)$
31.	$(-50) \div (+10)$	**32.**	$(+54) \div (-6)$	**33.**	$(-56) \div (-8)$
34.	$(+60) \div (+6)$	**35.**	$(+63) \div (-9)$	**36.**	$(-64) \div (-8)$
37.	$(-72) \div (+12)$	**38.**	$(+77) \div (+7)$	**39.**	$(-80) \div (+20)$
40.	$(+81) \div (-9)$	**41.**	$(-84) \div (-12)$	**42.**	$(+96) \div (+6)$
43.	$(-100) \div (-10)$	**44.**	$(-121) \div (+11)$	**45.**	$(+144) \div (-12)$
46.	$(-120) \div (+20)$	**47.**	$(-96) \div (-24)$	**48.**	$(+81) \div (-27)$

17 Algebra – use of brackets

Algebraic expressions are sometimes contained in brackets, like this:

$$(a + 2b + 3c)$$

Several such expressions may have to be added, like this:

$$(a + 2b + 3c) + (2a - 3b + c) + (3a + b - 2c)$$

or subtracted, like this:

$$(3a - 2b + 4c) - (2a - 3b + 4c)$$

Before addition or subtraction can take place, the brackets round the expressions must be removed. As the brackets are removed, the **Rule of Signs** must work between **the sign outside the bracket and each sign within the bracket.**

NOTE When a term or expression has no sign attached to it the quantity is always positive. You must think of it as having a plus (+) sign before it.

Let us reconsider the above expressions and **think** the missing signs into place:

```
 ( a + 2b + 3c)
↗ ↖
+   +
```

```
 ( a + 2b + 3c) + ( 2a – 3b + c) + ( 3a + b – 2c)
↗ ↖                 ↖                ↖
+   +                 +                +
```

```
 ( 3a – 2b + 4c) – ( 2a – 3b + 4c)
↗ ↖                  ↖
+   +                  +
```

EXAMPLE 1

$$(a + 2b + 3c) + (2a - 3b + c) + (3a + b - 2c)$$

$$= a + 2b + 3c + 2a - 3b + c + 3a + b - 2c$$

$$\text{Ans} = \underline{6a + 2c}$$

EXAMPLE 2

$$(3a - 2b + 4c) - (2a - 3b + 4c$$
$$= 3a - 2b + 4c - 2a + 3b - 4c$$
$$\text{Ans} = \underline{a + b}$$

NOTE

1 If a + sign goes before a bracket, the sign of each term within the bracket remains unchanged when the bracket is removed:

$$+ (2a - 3b + c) = + 2a - 3b + c$$

2 If a − sign goes before a bracket, the sign of each term within the bracket is changed when the bracket is removed:

$$- (2a - 3b + 4x) = - 2a + 3b - 4c$$

Here are some easy examples to start with:

Exercise 74

Simplify the following expressions by removing brackets; don't forget the **Rule of Signs**:

1.	$-(a+b)$	**2.**	$+(a+b)$	**3.**	$-(a-b)$
4.	$+(a-b)$	**5.**	$-(-a+b)$	**6.**	$-(-a-b)$
7.	$+(-a+b)$	**8.**	$+(-a-b)$	**9.**	$-(x-y)$
10.	$-(-x+y)$	**11.**	$-(x+y)$	**12.**	$-(-x-y)$
13.	$+(-x-y)$	**14.**	$+(2x-3y)$	**15.**	$-(3x-2y)$
16.	$+(-3x+2y)$	**17.**	$-(-3x-2y)$	**18.**	$+(-3x+2y)$

19.	$-(2a+2b-2c)$	**20.**	$+(-2a-2b+2c)$
21.	$-(-3a+b-2c)$	**22.**	$+(2a-3b+c)$
23.	$+(-a-2b-3c)$	**24.**	$-(4a+b-3c)$
25.	$-(-5x+2y-3z)$	**26.**	$+(3x-4y+2z)$
27.	$+(-x-3y-5z)$	**28.**	$-(-5x+3y-z)$
29.	$-(x+y+z)$	**30.**	$+(x-2y+4z)$

Exercise 75

Simplify the following:

1. $(a+b+c)+(2a+3b-c)+(a-2b+2c)$
2. $2a-b-c)+(-a+b+c)+(-a+b+c)$
3. $(-3a+2b-2c)+(a-b+c)+(2a-b+c)$
4. $(3a-3b-3c)+(-2a+b+c)+(-a+2b+c)$
5. $(2a+3b-2c)+(a-b+c)+(-3a-4b+c)$

6. $(4a - 3b + c) + (-3a + b - c) + (a + 4b + c)$
7. $(2a - 3b - c) + (a + 3b + 4c) + (a - b - 2c)$
8. $(3a + 2b + 3c) + (2a - b - 2c) + (-5a - b + c)$
9. $(3a + 4b - 2c) + (3a + 2b + 2c) + (-a + b - c)$
10. $(2a - 3b + 3c) + (3a - 2b - 3c) + (-4a + 3b - 4c)$
11. $(a + 2b - 4c) + (3a + 2b - c) + (-2a - 3b + 2c)$
12. $(-2a + b + 3c) + (-4a + 2b + 2c) + (2a - b + c)$

Exercise 76

Simplify the following: (*take care!*)

1. $(4a + 4b + c) - (2a + 3b + c)$
2. $(4a + 4b + c) - (3a - 2b + 2c)$
3. $(4a + 4b + c) - (-a + b - 3c)$
4. $(-4a - 4b - c) - (-4a - 4b - c)$
5. $(2a - 2b + c) - (3a - 4b - c)$
6. $(a - 2b + 2c) - (2a + 3b - c)$
7. $(2a + 2b + 3c) - (a + b - 2c)$
8. $(4a - 3b - 2c) - (3a - b - 2c)$
9. $(3a + 2b + 4c) - (2a - 2b + 2c)$
10. $(a - 3b - 2c) - (-3a + 2b - 4c)$
11. $(-2a + 4b - c) - (-4a - 2b + 3c)$
12. $(-3a - 2b + c) - (-3a - 2b + c)$

Exercise 77

Simplify the following: (*take extra care!*)

1. $(a + b) + (2a + b) - (a + 2b)$
2. $(a + 2b) + (2a + 3b) - (2a + 2b)$
3. $(2a + b) + (3a + 2b) - (a + b)$
4. $(a + b) + (2a + 2b) - (3a + 3b)$
5. $(2a - b) + (3a - 2b) - (2a - 3b)$
6. $(-3a + 2b) + (-2a + 3b) - (3a - 3b)$
7. $(-4a - b) + (-3a - 2b) - (-2a - 4b)$
8. $(-a + b) + (a - b) - (-a + b)$
9. $(4a + 4b) - (a + b) - (a + b)$
10. $(3a + 3b) - (a - b) - (-a + b)$
11. $(-4a - 2b) - (-2a - 2b) + (a + b)$
12. $(5a - 3b) - (3a - b) + (-a + 2b)$
13. $(2a + 3b + c) + (a + 2b - 3c) - (3a - 4b + 2c)$
14. $(3a - 4b + 2c) + (2a + 4b - c) - (a - 3b + c)$
15. $(2a + 2b - 2c) + (a - 3b + c) - (a - b + c)$
16. $(3a - 4b - 2c) - (-2a + b - 3c) - (a - 3b - 2c)$

Use of brackets in multiplication

Consider the expression 4 (a – b)

NOTE **Everything** inside the brackets must be multiplied by the 4 outside.

QUESTIONS

A What kind of a 4 is it? +4 or –4?
B What kind of 'a' is it inside the bracket? +a or –a?

REMEMBER

When no sign is given, the quantity is positive (+) and you must **think** a plus sign (+) into place.

EXAMPLE 1 $4(a - b) = \underline{4a - 4b}$

STEPS: + 4 times + a gives + 4a
+ 4 times –b gives –4b

EXAMPLE 2 $-6(2x - 3y) = \underline{-12x + 18y}$

STEPS: –6 times + 2x gives – 12x
–6 times –3y gives + 18y

EXAMPLE 3 $a(a - b) = \underline{a^2 - ab}$

STEPS: + a times + a gives + a^2
+ a times –b gives –ab

EXAMPLE 4 $-3a(2a - 4) = \underline{-6a^2 + 12a}$

STEPS: –3a times + 2a gives $-6a^2$
–3a times –4 gives + 12a

Exercise 78

Simplify the following:

1.	2(a + b)	**2.**	3(a + b)	**3.**	4(a + b)
4.	5(a – b)	**5.**	6(a – b)	**6.**	7(a – b)
7.	2(a + 3)	**8.**	3(a + 4)	**9.**	4(a + 5)
10.	5(a – 2)	**11.**	6(a – 3)	**12.**	7(a – 4)
13.	–2(a + b)	**14.**	–3(a + b)	**15.**	–4(a + b)
16.	–5(a – b)	**17.**	–6(a – b)	**18.**	–7(a – b)
19.	–2(a + 2)	**20.**	–3(a + 3)	**21.**	–4(a + 4)

22.	$-5(a-2)$	**23.**	$-6(a-3)$	**24.**	$-7(a-4)$
25.	$a(a+b)$	**26.**	$a(a+2b)$	**27.**	$a(2a+b)$
28.	$a(2a+2b)$	**29.**	$a(a-2b)$	**30.**	$a(-2a+b)$
31.	$2a(a+b)$	**32.**	$2a(a-b)$	**33.**	$2a(2a+2b)$
34.	$2a(2a-2b)$	**35.**	$2a(2a+3b)$	**36.**	$2a(3a-2b)$
37.	$-2a(a-b)$	**38.**	$-2a(2a-b)$	**39.**	$-2a(-a+2b)$
40.	$-3a(2a+3)$	**41.**	$-3a(2a-3)$	**42.**	$-3a(-2a-3)$
43.	$-2a(2a-4)$	**44.**	$4a(-3a+2)$	**45.**	$-4a(-2a-3)$
46.	$-5a(a+3)$	**47.**	$-5a(-2a-4)$	**48.**	$5a(-3a+2)$

Use of brackets in equations

NOTE Each side of the equation must be simplified by removing brackets before moving terms.

EXAMPLE Solve the equation: $5(x-2) = 2(2x+3)$

Remove brackets	$5x-10$	$=$	$4x+6$
Subtract 4x from both sides:	$x-10$	$=$	6
Add 10 to both sides:	x	$=$	16

NOTE The accuracy of the answer may be checked by substituting the value $x = 16$ in both sides of the original equation. If the answer is correct, both sides of the equation will have the same value.

CHECK When $x = 16$

LHS	$=$	$5(x-2)$	RHS	$=$	$2(2x+3)$
	$=$	$5(16-2)$		$=$	$2(32+3)$
	$=$	$5(14)$		$=$	$2(35)$
	$=$	70		$=$	70

$\therefore$ LHS = RHS

Exercise 79

Solve the following equations (*check your answers*):

1.	$2(x+1) = x+8$	**2.**	$2(x-1) = x+5$
3.	$2(x+2) = x+6$	**4.**	$2(x-2) = x+4$
5.	$3(x+1) = x+5$	**6.**	$3(x-3) = x+3$
7.	$3(x+2) = x+10$	**8.**	$3(x-2) = x+2$
9.	$4(x+1) = x+13$	**10.**	$4(x-2) = x+1$
11.	$2(x-1) = x+1$	**12.**	$2(x-1) = x-1$
13.	$2(x-2) = x+2$	**14.**	$2(x-2) = x-2$

15. $3(x-1) = x-1$

16. $3(x-2) = x+4$

17. $4(x-1) = x-10$

18. $4(x-2) = x-17$

19. $3x = 2(5-x)$

20. $12 = 2(8-2x)$

21. $3(2x-5) = 9$

22. $2x = 4(6-x)$

23. $3(x-1) = 2(x+3)$

24. $2(2x-1) = 3(x+2)$

25. $3(2x+3) = 5(1+x)$

26. $4(3-2x) = 3(6-4x)$

27. $7(x-3) = 3(7+x)$

28. $6(2x-7) = 7(x+6)$

29. $3(3x+2) = 2(4x+2)$

30. $4(2x-3) = 2(3x-2)$

Multiplication using two pairs of brackets

Sometimes we need to multiply the contents of two pairs of brackets as in this example:

$$(a+2)(a+3)$$

This situation means that $(a+3)$ has to be multiplied by **two** things; first, the 'a' (or more correctly '+a') and second, the '+2'.

<u>EXAMPLE 1</u> $(a+2)(a+3)$

STEP 1 $= a(a+3) + 2(a+3)$

STEP 2 $= a^2 + 3a + 2a + 6$

STEP 3 $= \underline{a^2 + 5a + 6}$

<u>STEPS IN CALCULATION</u>

1 Break the first bracket into separate terms, each with its correct sign, placing each in turn in front of the second bracket.

2 Multiply the second bracket by each term from the first bracket.

3 Collect like terms;

<u>EXAMPLE 2</u> $(2a-3)(a-4)$

$= 2a(a-4) - 3(a-4)$

$= 2a^2 - 8a - 3a + 12$

Ans $= \underline{2a^2 - 11a + 12}$

Exercise 80

Simplify the following:

1. $(a+1)(a+1)$

2. $(a+2)(a+2)$

3. $(a-1)(a-1)$

4. $(a-2)(a-2)$

5. $(a+1)(a-1)$

6. $(a+2)(a-2)$

7. $(a+1)(a+2)$

8. $(a-1)(a-2)$

9. $(a+1)(a-2)$

10. $(a-1)(a+2)$

11.	$(a+2)(a+3)$	**12.**	$(a-2)(a-3)$
13.	$(a+2)(a-3)$	**14.**	$(a-2)(a+3)$
15.	$(a+3)(a+3)$	**16.**	$(a-3)(a-3)$
17.	$(a+3)(a-3)$	**18.**	$(a-3)(a+3)$
19.	$(a+3)(a-4)$	**20.**	$(a-3)(a+4)$
21.	$(2a+1)(a+1)$	**22.**	$(2a-1)(a-1)$
23.	$(2a+1)(a-2)$	**24.**	$(2a-1)(a+2)$
25.	$(2a-2)(a-2)$	**26.**	$(2a+3)(2a-1)$
27.	$(2a-3)(a+2)$	**28.**	$(2a-3)(2a-3)$
29.	$(2a+3)(2a+4)$	**30.**	$(2a-4)(3a-2)$
31.	$(2a-1)(3a+2)$	**32.**	$(3a-2)(a+4)$
33.	$(2a+3)(3a+4)$	**34.**	$(a-4)(4a+3)$
35.	$(3a+2)(3a-2)$	**36.**	$(3a+4)(4a-3)$
37.	$(-a+2)(a+1)$	**38.**	$(-a+1)(a+2)$
39.	$(-a+1)(a+3)$	**40.**	$(-a+2)(a-2)$
41.	$(-a+1)(-a+1)$	**42.**	$(-a+1)(-a+2)$
43.	$(-a+2)(-a+3)$	**44.**	$(-a+3)(-a+4)$
45.	$(-a-2)(a+1)$	**46.**	$(-a-1)(a+2)$
47.	$(-a-1)(-a-2)$	**48.**	$(-a-2)(-a-3)$
49.	$(-2a+1)(a+2)$	**50.**	$(-2a+2)(a+3)$
51.	$(-a+2)(2a+3)$	**52.**	$(-a+3)(2a+4)$
53.	$(-2a+1)(-a+2)$	**54.**	$(-2a+3)(2a-3)$
55.	$(3a-4)(2a+5)$	**56.**	$(5a-2)(4a-3)$
57.	$(-3a+1)(-2a+3)$	**58.**	$(-4a-3)(-3a-4)$
59.	$(5a-3)(-4a+5)$	**60.**	$(3a+4)(3a-4)$

Substitution

EXAMPLE 1 If $a = 4$, find the value of $(a+2)(a+3)$

If $a = 4$, $(a+2)(a+3) = (4+2)(4+3)$

$= 6 \times 7$

Ans $= \underline{42}$

EXAMPLE 2 If $a = 2$, find the value of $(2a-3)(a-4)$

If $a = 2$, $(2a-3)(a-4) = (4-3)(2-4)$

$= 1 \times -2$

Ans $= \underline{-2}$

Exercise 81

Find the value of each expression in Exercise 80 using the following values of 'a':

In questions 1 to 20 let a = 2
In questions 21 to 40 let a = 3
In questions 41 to 60 let a = 4

18 Volume

Cubes and cuboids – revision

$$V = L \times B \times H$$

Exercise 82

Find the volume of each of the following cuboids:

1. 2m by 2m by 2m
2. 3m by 3m by 3m
3. 2m by 3m by 4m
4. 3m by 4m by 5m
5. 5cm by 6cm by 7cm
6. 4cm by 5cm by 8cm
7. $2\frac{1}{2}$cm by 4cm by 10cm
8. $2\frac{1}{4}$cm by 4cm by 8cm
9. $3\frac{1}{3}$cm by 6cm by 8cm
10. $4\frac{1}{5}$cm by 5cm by 6cm
11. 2·2dm by 5dm by 10dm
12. 3·5dm by 4dm by 5dm

Solids of uniform cross-section

A **section** is the shape we see when we cut through an object. The shaded area shown in the diagram is a section taken through a T-shaped girder. The distance AB is called the length. The shape of a section is affected by the angle at which the cut is made through the object. The following diagrams show two different sections taken through a cylindrical object like a stick of rock.

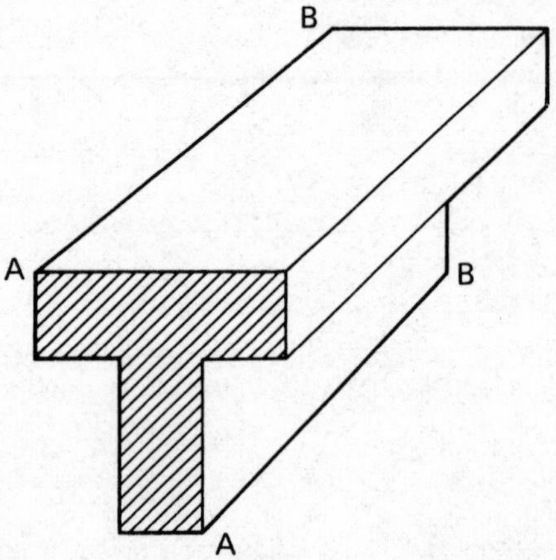

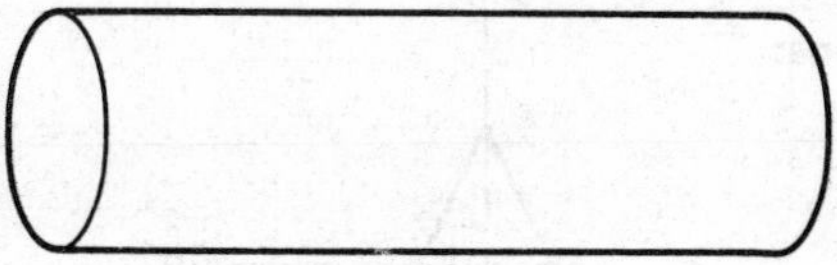

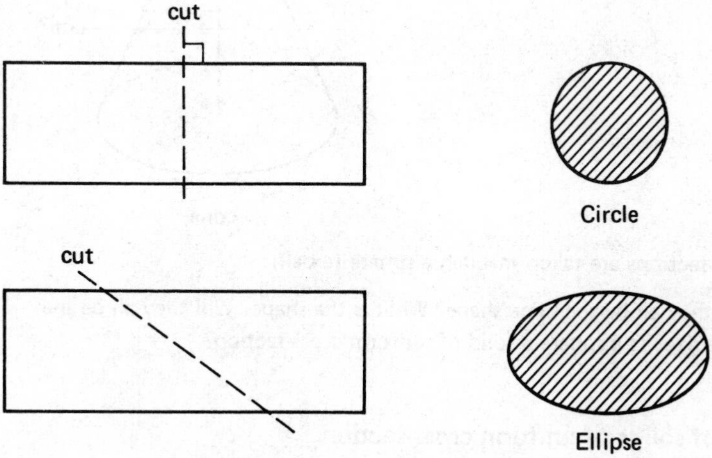

Cylinder Section

In our present work we shall always assume that our 'slices' (sections) are taken **at right-angles to the length**; they are then known as **cross-sections.** When all cross-sections through a solid are of **the same shape and size** they are said to be **uniform**, and the solid is then described as **a solid of uniform cross-section.**

SOMETHING TO DO

1 Make sketches of the cross-sections through the following: a paving stone, a water-pipe, a ruler, a swiss roll, a tree-trunk, a new pencil, a railway line, a railway sleeper, a cucumber, a thick rope.
2 When you next have some bananas or a cucumber at home, ask mother to allow you to make different cuts through them to compare the sections.

QUESTIONS

1 If cross-sections are taken through a **cone**:

Will they all be the same shape?
What is the shape?
Will they all be the same size?
Is a cone a solid of uniform cross-section?

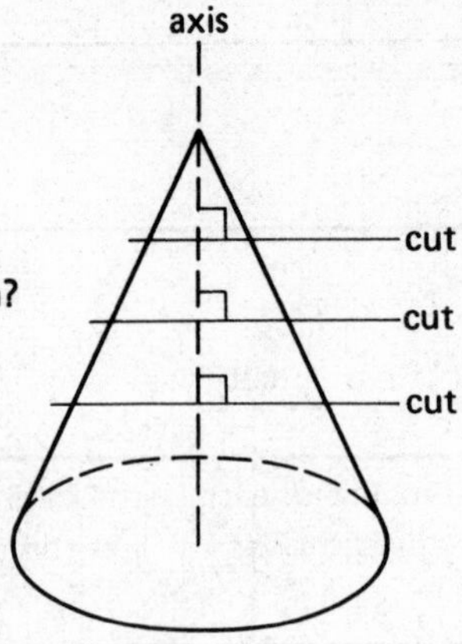

cone

2 If cross-sections are taken through a **sphere** (a ball):

Will they all be the same shape? What is the shape? Will they all be the same size? Is a sphere a solid of uniform cross-section?

Volume of solids of uniform cross-section

VOLUME = AREA OF CROSS-SECTION X LENGTH

EXAMPLE Find the volume of the uniform solid shown in the diagram. All corners are right-angled and dimensions are in cm.

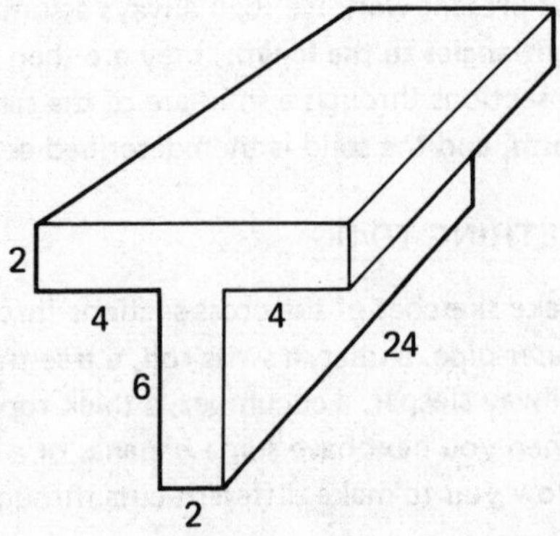

To find the area of cross-section:

AREA A = (10 X 2) = 20cm^2
AREA B = (6 X 2) = 12cm^2

Area of cross-section = 32cm^2

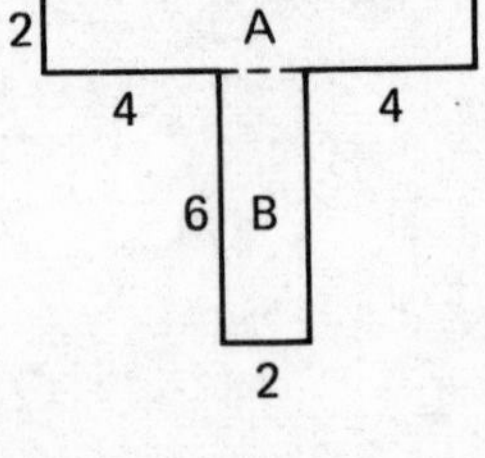

To find volume:

			CALCULATION
Volume	=	area of cross-section X length	32
	=	$32cm^2$ X 24cm	24
Ans	=	$\underline{768cm^3}$	640
			128
			768

Exercise 83

Find the volume of each of the following uniform solids. All corners are right-angled and dimensions are in centimetres:

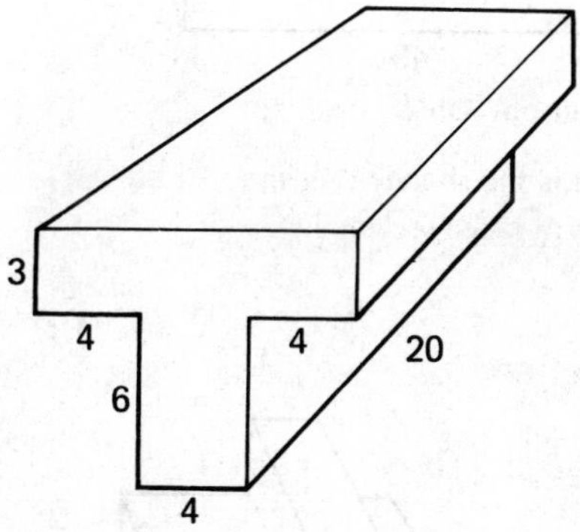

1

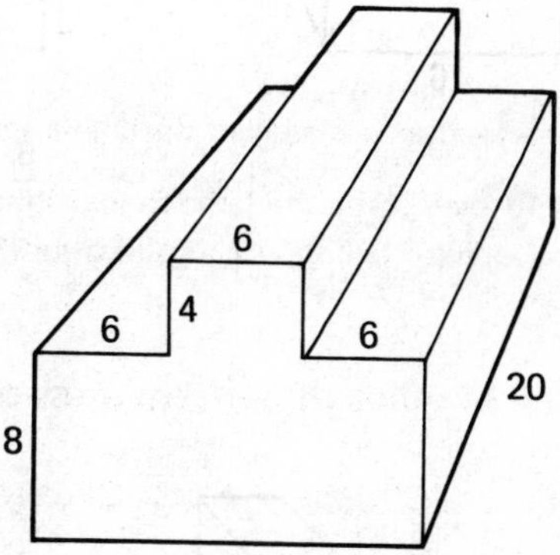

2

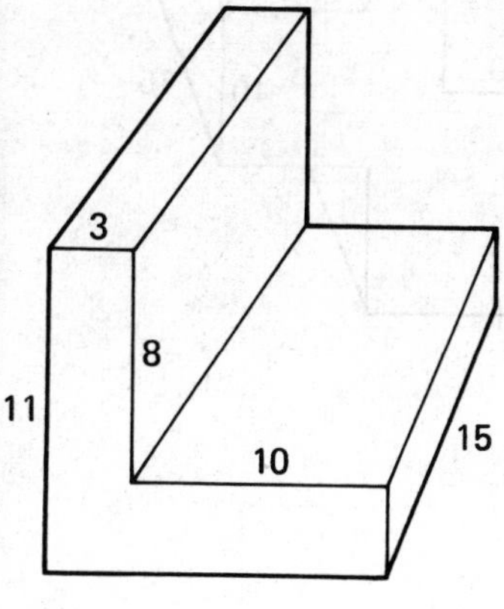

3

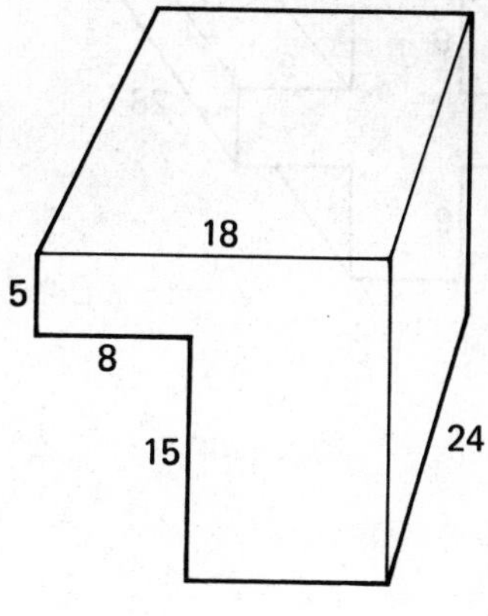

4

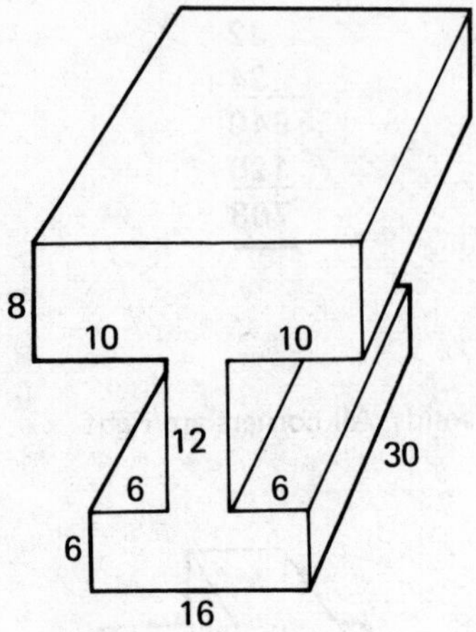
8
10
10
12
30
6
6
6
16

5

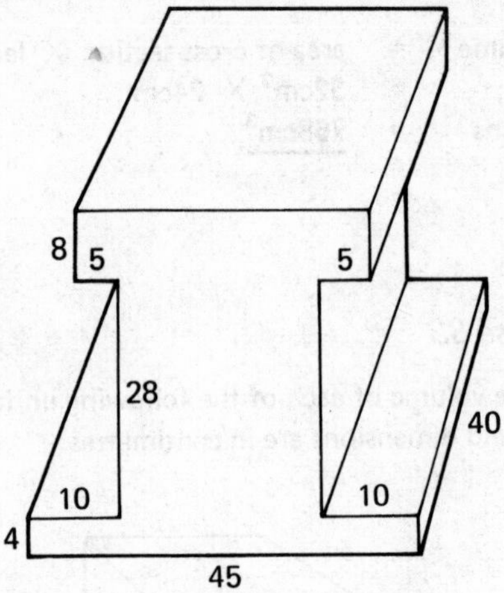
8
5
5
28
40
10
10
4
45

6

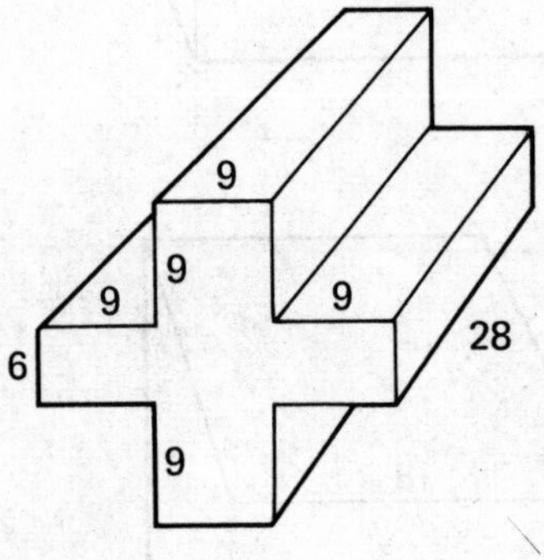
9
9
9
9
6
28
9

7

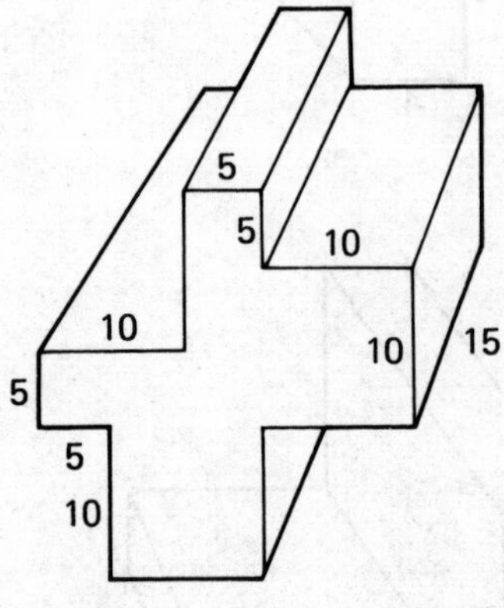
5
5
10
10
10
5
15
5
10

8

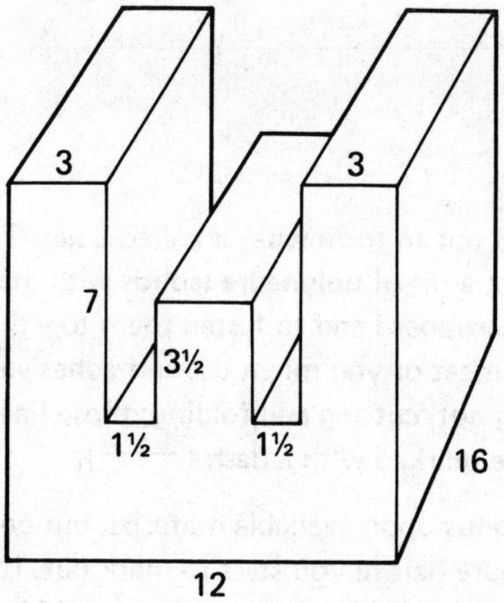

9

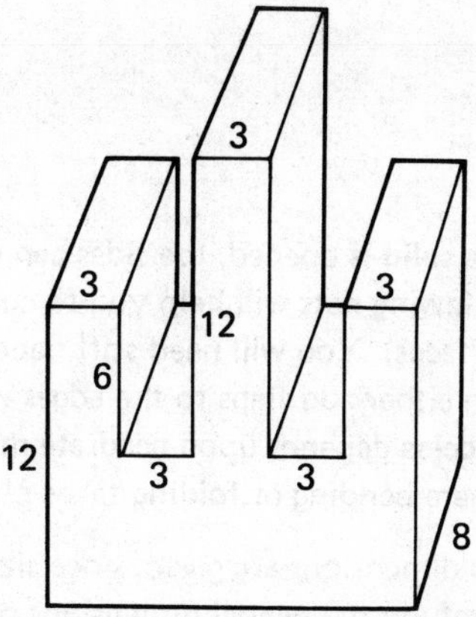

10

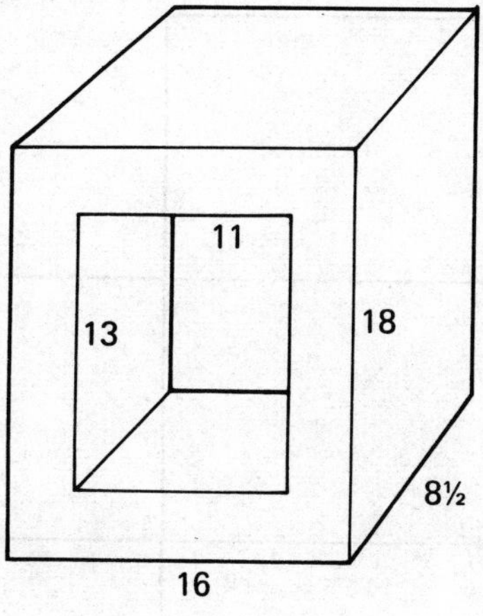

11

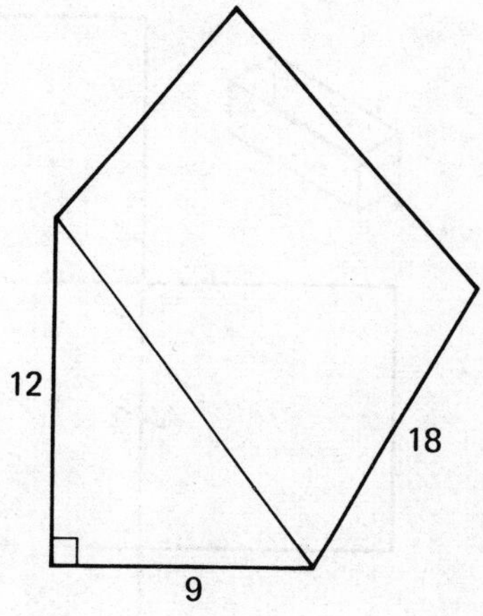

12

19 Construction of solids

If a **solid** is opened, the sides can be laid out to form what is called a **net**. The following nets will help you to construct a set of **polyhedra** (solids with many surfaces). You will need stiff paper or cardboard and to fasten them together you can either add flaps to the edges which meet or you might use self-adhesive tape. Success depends upon accurate marking out, cutting and folding; those lines where bending or folding takes place are marked with a dash (—/—).

No dimensions are given, since size depends upon available material, but consider carefully the overall dimensions of a figure **before** you start to mark out. It may be possible to trace the nets or the basic pattern shapes given on page **104**.

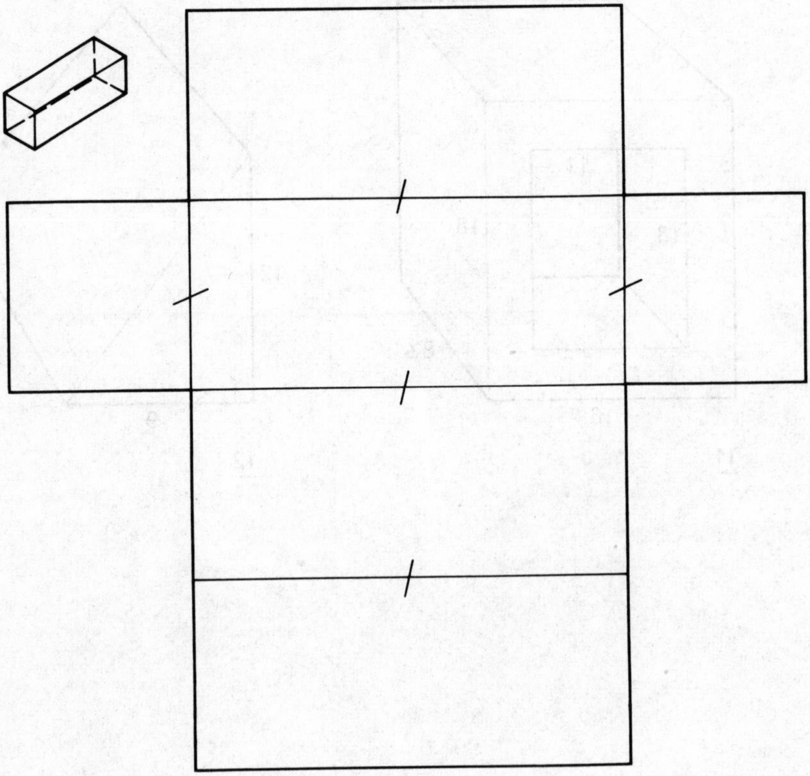

Rectangular prism

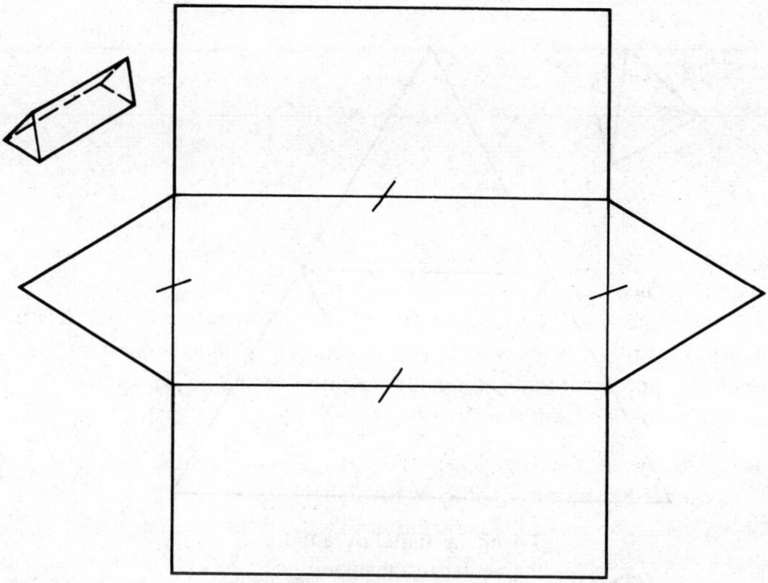

Triangular prism

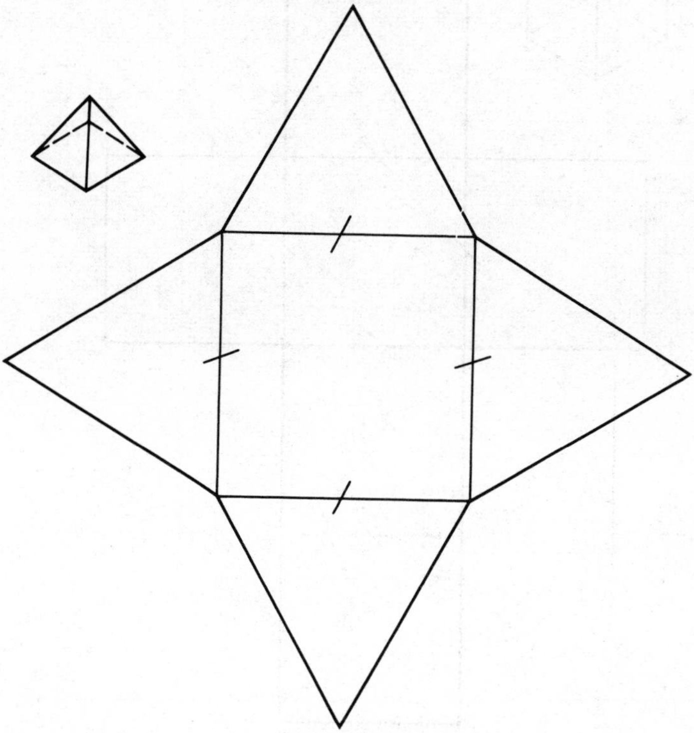

Square-based pyramid

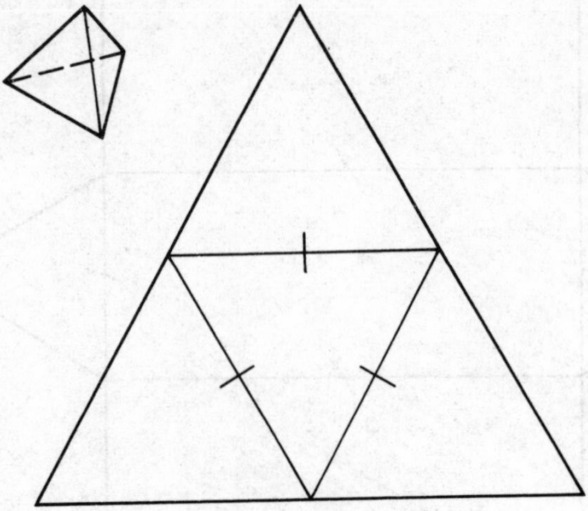

Triangular-based pyramid
(regular tetrahedron)
(four surfaces)

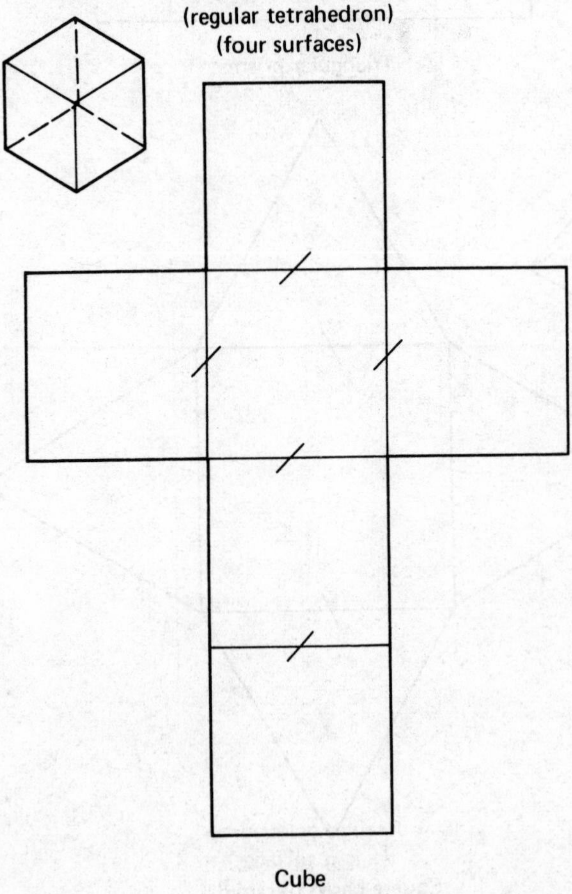

Cube
(six-surfaces)

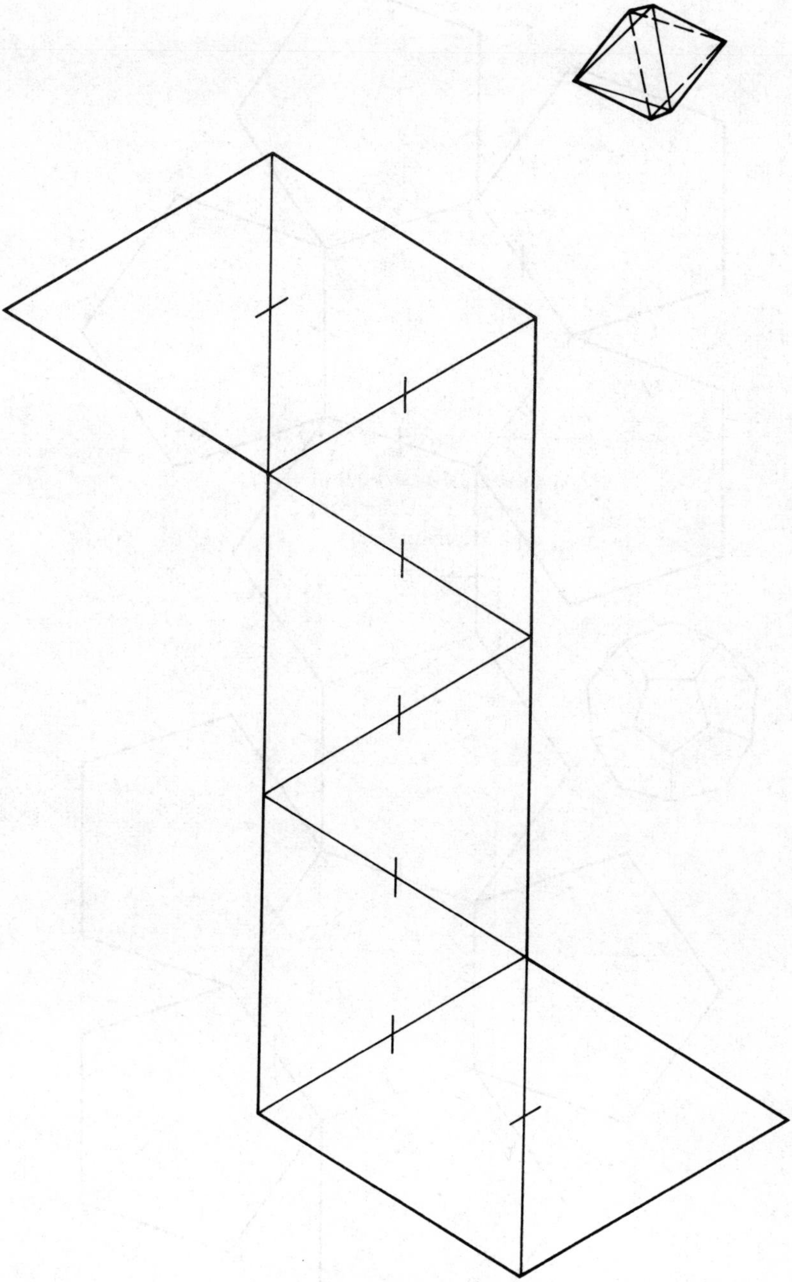

Regular octahedron
(eight surfaces)

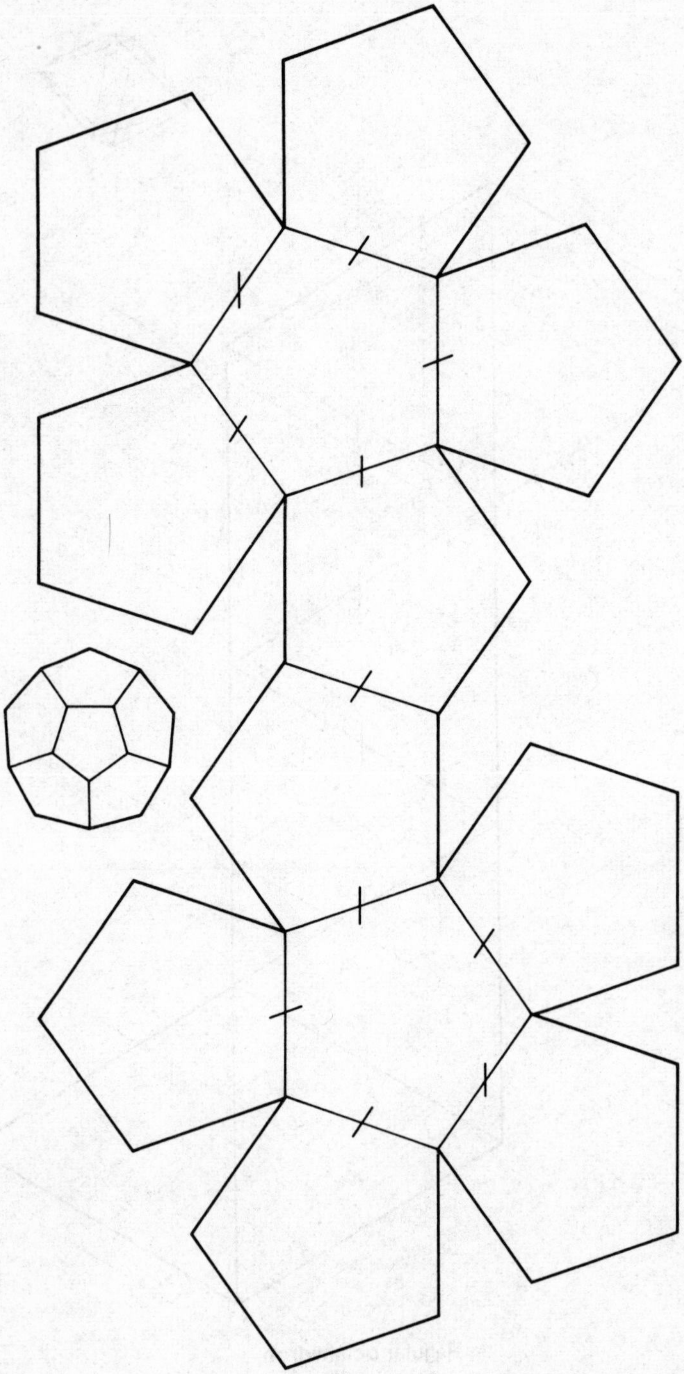

Regular dodecahedron
(twelve surfaces)

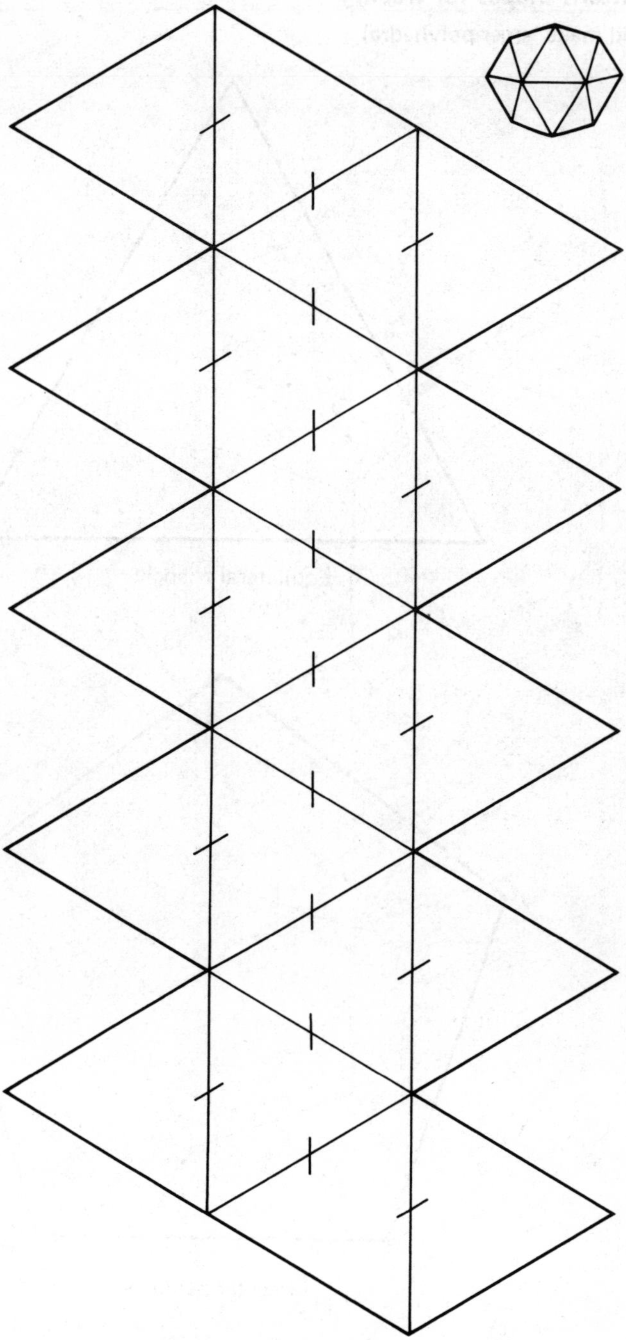

Regular icosahedron
(twenty surfaces)

Basic pattern shapes for tracing

(These will make larger polyhedra)

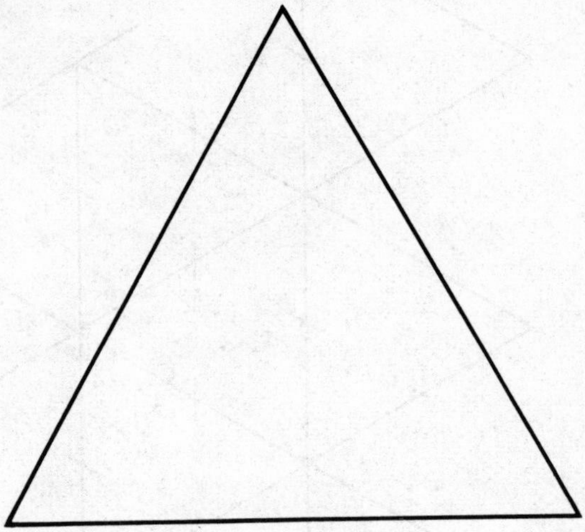

Equilateral triangle

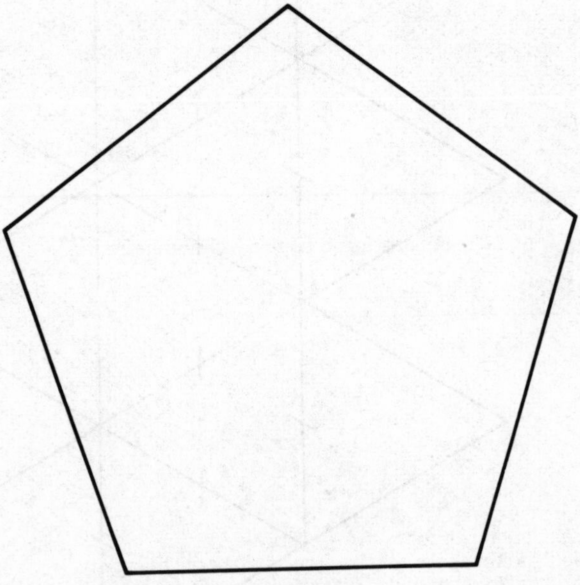

Regular pentagon

20 Using a ready-reckoner

Ready-reckoners were often used by shop-keepers or tradesmen to help them to calculate the total cost of goods sold or used on a job. These days modern cash registers and pocket calculators are used instead. Nevertheless, let us try to use a simple form of ready-reckoner shown on page 107.

Money values are given across the top and the number required appears down the left hand side. It will be necessary to break the money (and perhaps the number required) into suitable parts that can be found from the table.

<u>EXAMPLE</u> Find the cost of 23 articles at £4.35½

STEPS	1.	23 at £4	=	£92
	2.	23 at 30p	=	6.90
	3.	23 at 5p	=	1.15
	4.	23 at ½p	=	11½
	5.	TOTAL COST	=	£100.16½

<u>NOTE</u> **You** must decide where the decimal point belongs to give £s.

Exercise 84

Using the ready-reckoner:

Find the cost of **17** articles at each of the following prices:

1. 78½p **2.** £3.49 **3.** £7.24½ **4.** £15.62

Find the cost of **25** articles at each of the following prices:

5. 65p **6.** £7.31½ **7.** £13.48 **8.** £32.59½

Find the cost of **34** articles at each of the following prices:

9. 30½p **10.** £4.50 **11.** £18 **12.** £34

Find the cost of **55** articles at each of the following prices:

3. 50p **14.** £5.05½ **15.** £15 **16.** £55

Find the cost of **71** articles at each of the following prices:

17. 7½p **18.** £1.03 **19.** £7.40½ **20.** £12.50

Using the prices given in the catalogue:

Find the cost of **12** of each of the following items:

21. CB 6 **22.** CM 7 **23.** CW 21 **24.** F 2

Find the cost of **20** of each of the following items:

25. CG 1 **26.** CW 8 **27.** HW 14 **28.** L 4

Find the cost of **68** of each of the following items:

29. CB 14 **30.** CM 2 **31.** CW 4 **32.** CW 20
33. F 5 **34.** F 12 **35.** HW 19 **36.** HW 21

READY RECKONER   Cost in pence or £s

No.	½	1	2	3	4	5	6	7	8	9	10	20	30	40	50
1	0·5	1	2	3	4	5	6	7	8	9	10	20	30	40	50
2	1	2	4	6	8	10	12	14	16	18	20	40	60	80	100
3	1·5	3	6	9	12	15	18	21	24	27	30	60	90	120	150
4	2	4	8	12	16	20	24	28	32	36	40	80	120	160	200
5	2·5	5	10	15	20	25	30	35	40	45	50	100	150	200	250
6	3	6	12	18	24	30	36	42	48	54	60	120	180	240	300
7	3·5	7	14	21	28	35	42	49	56	63	70	140	210	280	350
8	4	8	16	24	32	40	48	56	64	72	80	160	240	320	400
9	4·5	9	18	27	36	45	54	63	72	81	90	180	270	360	450
10	5	10	20	30	40	50	60	70	80	90	100	200	300	400	500
11	5·5	11	22	33	44	55	66	77	88	99	110	220	330	440	550
12	6	12	24	36	48	60	72	84	96	108	120	240	360	480	600
13	6·5	13	26	39	52	65	78	91	104	117	130	260	390	520	650
14	7	14	28	42	56	70	84	98	112	126	140	280	420	560	700
15	7·5	15	30	45	60	75	90	105	120	135	150	300	450	600	750
16	8	16	32	48	64	80	96	112	128	144	160	320	480	640	800
17	8·5	17	34	51	68	85	102	119	136	153	170	340	510	680	850
18	9	18	36	54	72	90	108	126	144	162	180	360	540	720	900
19	9·5	19	38	57	76	95	114	133	152	171	190	380	570	760	950
20	10	20	40	60	80	100	120	140	160	180	200	400	600	800	1000
21	10·5	21	42	63	84	105	126	147	168	189	210	420	630	840	1050
22	11	22	44	66	88	110	132	154	176	198	220	440	660	880	1100
23	11·5	23	46	69	92	115	138	161	184	207	230	460	690	920	1150
24	12	24	48	72	96	120	144	168	192	216	240	480	720	960	1200
25	12·5	25	50	75	100	125	150	175	200	225	250	500	750	1000	1250
26	13	26	52	78	104	130	156	182	208	234	260	520	780	1040	1300
27	13·5	27	54	81	108	135	162	189	216	243	270	540	810	1080	1350
28	14	28	56	84	112	140	168	196	224	252	280	560	840	1120	1400
29	14·5	29	58	87	116	145	174	203	232	261	290	580	870	1160	1450
30	15	30	60	90	120	150	180	210	240	270	300	600	900	1200	1500
40	20	40	80	120	160	200	240	280	320	360	400	800	1200	1600	2000
50	25	50	100	150	200	250	300	350	400	450	500	1000	1500	2000	2500
60	30	60	120	180	240	300	360	420	480	540	600	1200	1800	2400	3000
70	35	70	140	210	280	350	420	490	560	630	700	1400	2100	2800	3500
80	40	80	160	240	320	400	480	560	640	720	800	1600	2400	3200	4000
90	45	90	180	270	360	450	540	630	720	810	900	1800	2700	3600	4500
100	50	100	200	300	400	500	600	700	800	900	1000	2000	3000	4000	5000

21 Algebra – problems

Some brain-teasers to finish the book

Exercise 85

1 Benjamin has x marbles in one pocket and y marbles in another:
(a) How many marbles has he altogether?
(b) Nicholas has twice as many, how many has he?
(c) How many have they altogether?

2 A box weighs 2kg when empty. What is the total weight if it contains x kg of apples? What is the total weight of 6 boxes of apples?

3 A barrel will hold G litres. I pour in g litres. How many litres are required to fill it?

4 Rebecca has a number of coins, x of them are 50p coins and 6 are 10p coins:
(a) How many coins has she altogether?
(b) How much money has she in pence?
(c) How much money has she in pounds?

5 A fence is supported by posts f metres apart:
(a) How long is a fence containing 60 posts?
(b) How many posts are required in a fence 60m long?

6 What is the area of each of the rectangles A, B, C and D? What is the total area? The dimensions are in centimetres.

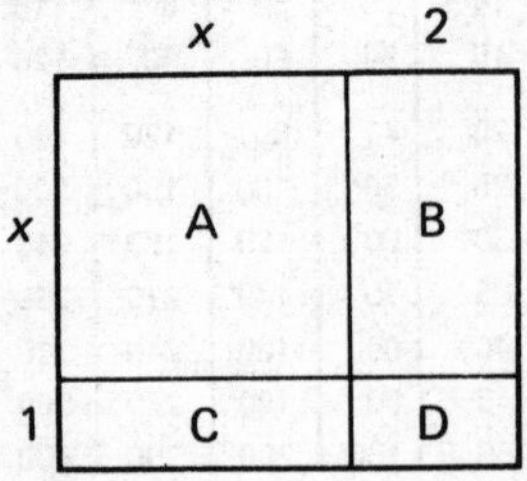

7 What is the area of the complete rectangle? What is the area of the shaded portion? The dimensions are in centimetres.

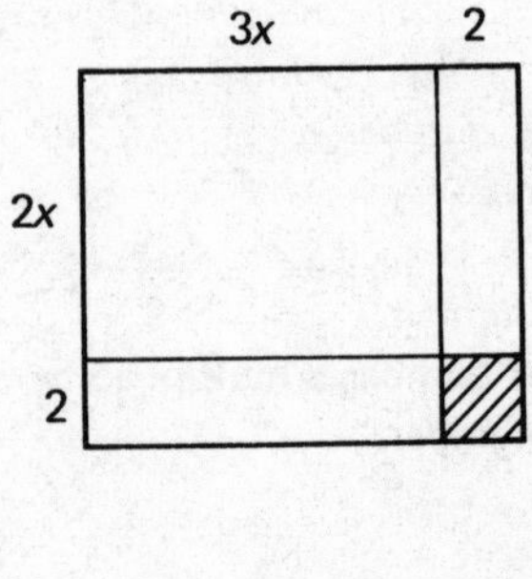

8 Joanna has 15 coins, Emma has 31 coins and Elizabeth has 14 coins. They have £6 altogether. If the coins are all of the same value, what is the value of one coin? If the total value of the coins is 30p, what would be the value of one coin?

9 By how much is 5 greater than 2?

10 By how much is 5 greater than x?

11 By how much is 6 less than 10?

12 By how much is 6 less than y?

13 By how much does a exceed b?

14 By how much is x less than y?

15 What must be added to x to make 8?

16 What must be added to 8 to make y?

17 What must be added to b to make a?

18 What must be added to x to make y?

19 One number is x, another is y. What is (a) their sum, (b) their difference, (c) their product?

20 The sum of two numbers is 16 and one of them is x; what is the other?

21 The difference between two numbers is 12 and the larger is y; what is the other?

22 There are three numbers each equal to x: (a) what is their sum? (b) what is their product?

23 There are three consecutive numbers of which 6 is the smallest; what are the others?

24 There are four consecutive numbers of which 6 is the largest; what are the others?

25 x is a number, when it is halved the result is 6; what is the number?

26 x is a number, when it is halved the result is 18; what is the number?

27 x is a number, when it is doubled that result is 16; what is the number?

28 x is a number, when it is trebled the result is 27; what is the number?

29 x is a number, when 2 is added the result is 7; what is the number?

20 x is a number, when 5 is subtracted the result is 4; what is the number?

31 x is a number, it is doubled and 3 is added, the result is 11; what is the number?

32 x is a number, it is multiplied by 4 and 5 is subtracted, the result is 11; what is the number?

33 x is a number to which is added 3, this sum is multiplied by 4, the result is 20; what is the number?

34 x is a number, when 3 is subtracted the result is the same as when the number is subtracted from 3; what is the number?

35 A number is multiplied by 2 and 4 is added, the result is 12; find the number.

36 A number is multiplied by 5 and 7 is added, the result is 22; find the number.

37 A number is multiplied by 3 and 5 is subtracted, the result is 13; find the number.

38 A number is multiplied by 7 and 15 is subtracted, the result is -1; find the number.
39 The sum of two consecutive numbers is 27, find the numbers.
40 The sum of two consecutive numbers is 43, find the numbers.
41 The sum of two numbers is 15, their difference is 7; find the numbers.
42 The sum of two numbers is 28, their difference is 4; find the numbers.
43 Divide 36 into two numbers whose difference is 12.
44 Divide 47 into two numbers whose difference is 23.
45 The sum of three consecutive numbers is 36; find the numbers.

Catalogue

Boys' clothing

Ref No	*Description*	*Price*
CB 1	Parka jacket	£ 5.25
CB 2	Blazer (wool mixture)	£ 5.75
CB 3	Jeans (cotton)	£ 3.50
CB 4	Pullover (acrilan)	£ 3.10
CB 5	Pyjamas (cotton)	£ 2.25
CB 6	Raincoat (lightweight, nylon)	£ 2.29
CB 7	Shirt (drip-dry cotton)	£ 2.65
CB 8	Shoes	£ 5.25
CB 9	Trousers (terylene/wool)	£ 3.75
CB 10	Set of underwear	£ 1.05
CB 11	Socks (bri-nylon, 2 pairs)	75p
CB 12	Tie	60p
CB 13	Slippers	£ 1.75
CB 14	Handkerchief (cotton)	15p
CB 15	PE shoes (canvas)	£ 1.60
CB 16	Football boots (leather uppers)	£ 3.25

Girls' clothing

Ref No	*Description*	*Price*
CG 1	Anorak jacket	£ 3.89
CG 2	Blazer (wool mixture)	£ 5.50
CG 3	Blouse (nylon)	£ 2.50
CG 4	Dress (drip-dry cotton)	£ 2.49
CG 5	Gym tunic (rayon)	£ 2.85
CG 6	Jumper (orlon)	£ 2.20
CG 7	Nightdress (nylon)	£ 2.15
CG 8	Pyjamas (cotton)	£ 2.50
CG 9	Raincoat (terylene)	£10.25
CG 10	Shoes	£ 5.45

CG 11	Skirt (courtelle)	£ 3.45
CG 12	Set of underwear	£ 2.15
CG 13	Slippers	£ 1.20
CG 14	Handkerchief	12p

Men's clothing

Ref No	*Description*	*Price*
CM 1	Cardigan (crimplene)	£ 5.15
CM 2	Cardigan (wool)	£ 7.20
CM 3	Jacket (wool)	£16.50
CM 4	Pyjamas (cotton)	£ 4.25
CM 5	Raincoat (cotton/rayon)	£ 9.25
CM 6	Raincoat (nylon/wool)	£23.99
CM 7	Shirt (poplin)	£ 4.75
CM 8	Shirt (bri-nylon)	£ 3.75
CM 9	Shoes (suede)	£ 5.30
CM 10	Shoes (casual)	£10.99
CM 11	Shoes (heavy-duty)	£ 5.20
CM 12	Slacks (denim)	£ 4.65
CM 13	Suit (terylene/wool)	£31.25
CM 14	Trousers (crimplene)	£ 6.25
CM 15	Zip-jacket	£ 6.99
CM 16	Tie	£ 1.25
CM 17	Socks (wool/nylon, 2 pairs)	£ 1.15
CM 18	Set of underwear	£ 1.60
CM 19	Slippers	£ 2.15
CM 20	Handkerchief	20p

Women's clothing

Ref No	*Description*	*Price*
CW 1	Cardigan (tricel)	£ 3.15
CW 2	Cardigan (acrilan)	£ 5.35
CW 3	Coat (rayon/wool)	£14.20
CW 4	Dress (cotton)	£ 4.50
CW 5	Dress (crimplene)	£ 7.99
CW 6	Handbag (leather)	£ 9.25
CW 7	Handbag (plastic)	£ 3.15
CW 8	Nightdress (nylon)	£ 2.85
CW 9	Pyjamas (cotton)	£ 3.50

CW 10	Raincoat (terylene)	£12.20
CW 11	Sandals	£ 3.85
CW 12	Shoes	£ 8.20
CW 13	Skirt (terylene)	£ 6.20
CW 14	Skirt (tricel)	£ 2.50
CW 15	Slacks (crimplene)	£ 3.75
CW 16	Blouse (nylon)	£ 3.20
CW 17	Suit (2-piece, courtelle)	£14.20
CW 18	Set of underwear (cotton)	£ 1.80
CW 19	Set of underwear (nylon)	£ 2.20
CW 20	Tights (2 pairs)	85p
CW 21	Gloves (leather)	£ 3.85
CW 22	Handkerchief	14p
CW 23	Slippers	£ 2.20
CW 24	Umbrella	£ 4.15

Furniture

Ref No	*Description*	*Price*
F 1	Carpet square (2·5m by 3m)	£16.50
F 2	Carpet square (3m by 4m)	£43.20
F 3	Chest of drawers	£42.40
F 4	Convertible settee	£49.75
F 5	Dining chairs (set of 4)	£52.00
F 6	Dining table	£32.00
F 7	Divan and mattress (double)	£68.60
F 8	Divan and mattress (single)	£36.25
F 9	Double bunk with mattresses	£36.85
F 10	Dressing table	£52.50
F 11	Kitchen chairs (set of 4)	£19.40
F 12	Kitchen table	£16.40
F 13	Lounge chair	£31.15
F 14	Rug (2m by 1m)	£ 8.20
F 15	Sideboard	£45.00
F 16	Stair carpet 60cm wide (per metre length)	£ 2.75
F 17	Stair carpet 70cm wide (per metre length)	£ 4.20
F 18	Wardrobe	£56.00

Hardware

Ref No	*Description*	*Price*
HW 1	Canteen of cutlery (44 piece)	£26.30
HW 2	Carpet shampooer	£ 6.40
HW 3	Carpet sweeper	£ 7.20
HW 4	Dinner set (24 piece)	£ 9.95
HW 5	Electric fire	£14.40
HW 6	Electric fire (coal effect)	£21.65
HW 7	Electric iron (steam/dry)	£ 7.20
HW 8	Electric kettle	£ 8.50
HW 9	Fire guard	£ 4.20
HW 10	Food mixer	£48.50
HW 11	Gas kettle	£ 3.20
HW 12	Ironing board	£ 4.60
HW 13	Oil heater (radiant burner)	£23.50
HW 14	Oil heater (convector)	£19.45
HW 15	Refrigerator	£42.50
HW 16	Set of baking tins	£ 3.25
HW 17	Set of kitchen tools	£ 3.50
HW 18	Set of casseroles	£ 2.65
HW 19	Set of saucepans	£10.20
HW 20	Spin dryer	£28.50
HW 21	Tea set (21 piece)	£ 7.50
HW 22	Vacuum cleaner (cylinder)	£35.60
HW 23	Vacuum cleaner (upright)	£42.40
HW 24	Washing machine	£110.20

Leisure and pleasure

Ref No	*Description*	*Price*
L 1	Garden fork (stainless steel)	£ 5.20
L 2	Garden spade (stainless steel)	£ 5.60
L 3	Knitting wool (per 50gm ball)	30p
L 4	Record player and speakers (stereo)	£42.50
L 5	Tape-recorder (cassette)	£29.50
L 6	Radio (portable)	£11.70
L 7	Motorist's tool kit	£82.95
L 8	Sewing machine	£58.95
L 9	Typewriter	£28.85
L 10	Camera	£24.60